DOROTHY MULLIGAN
TE 6 - 2883

To All Thoughtful Persons and Patient Scholars

To all Thoughtful Persons,
White and colored,
Primitive and modern,
Who have stopped to wonder —
Who asked the great questions —
Who searched for true answers —
Who tried to imagine —
Who told their imaginings:
To all of these
We are deeply grateful.

To all Patient Scholars,
Who have searched old records —
Who have lived with strange peoples —
Who have learned strange languages —
Who listened to wise ones telling their tales
And wrote their words down
In books we could read
And retell to children:
To all of these
We are deeply grateful.

Sophia Lyon Fahs is the author of *From Long Ago and Many Lands; Jesus: The Carpenter's Son; The Old Story of Salvation;* and *Today's Children and Yesterday's Heritage.* She is also the co-author of *The Church Across the Street* and *Consider the Children: How They Grow.* Mrs. Fahs, who holds degrees from the College of Wooster, Columbia University, and Union Theological Seminary, taught at Union for seventeen years. For twenty-two years, until her retirement in 1951, she served the American Unitarian Association as part-time editor of children's materials; she is now Curriculum Consultant in the Department of Education of the Unitarian Universalist Association.

Dorothy T. Spoerl, formerly chairman of the psychology department at the American International College, Springfield, Massachusetts, has been principal of the Elementary School in Acworth, New Hampshire, and is now curriculum editor for the Department of Education of the Unitarian Universalist Association. She formerly worked in the textbook department of the Houghton Mifflin Company. She is an ordained Universalist minister.

BEGINNINGS:

EARTH   SKY   LIFE   DEATH

Stories, Ancient and Modern

by Sophia Lyon Fahs and Dorothy T. Spoerl

BEACON PRESS   BEACON HILL   BOSTON

Fifth printing, December 1965

Original illustrations by Gobin Stair

This book is a combination and revision of *Beginnings of Earth and Sky* by Sophia L. Fahs (Boston: Beacon Press, 1937) and *Beginnings of Life and Death* by Sophia L. Fahs and Dorothy T. Spoerl (Boston: Beacon Press, 1938).

Contents

Introduction

On a hilltop in West Africa in a little schoolhouse over-looking the sea, a class of boys and girls were studying quietly at their desks. Kofi seemed to be reading like the others.

The room was still. Outside the window a bird was singing. A rooster crowed. A dog barked. Kofi heard none of these sounds.

Presently he closed his book and looked up at his teacher. He caught her eye. He felt she would understand.

"Awura," he said, slowly and wonderingly;
"when you think how things are —
and you don't know how they began —
and how they will go on —
and you don't know whether they will end —
then you can go on thinking and thinking —
and never stop."

Who among us has not at some time felt as Kofi did that morning by the sea? Who was the first person to wonder how things began and how they will go on and whether or not they will end?

Perhaps as long as there have been stars in the sky and people who could look up and see them, men have been wondering. As long as there have been sunrises and sunsets, and people to watch them. As long as there have been seeds growing into flowers and trees, and people to remember their beginnings. As long as babies have been born and old people have died, and there have been people who loved them.

But some say: "What's the use of wondering about the way things began? What difference does it make anyway? We can never find out." So they soon stop wondering.

Others say: "We like the feel of wondering. We like trying to think of more things than we can see and understand. We like to imagine and dream of how things might have begun."

And still others say: "Perhaps we can find out more than we now know if we try." So they keep on asking, and exploring and studying.

Some of these stories about beginnings were told again and again for years before anyone was able to write them down. Some were lettered on clay or chiseled into stone. Some were written with pens on long rolls of sheepskin or papyrus. Some were told by people who never learned to write at all. They were told by the grandfathers and the grandmothers. Those who listened asked to hear them again and again. Children, when they grew up, told the same stories to their children.

Sometimes they sang the stories. Sometimes they danced them in pantomime. Those who watched the dancing beat time on hollow logs or clapped their hands. Sometimes they painted pictures of the stories on the walls of their caves or temples.

All the stories in this book, except the one from the scientists of today, were told before telescopes and microscopes had been invented. Without airplanes, steamships, and trains, only the very adventurous wandered far from home.

No people had explored the earth far from its own shores. The ancient people of Iceland knew nothing of the sunny plains of Africa or Australia. The Japanese thought their eight small islands surrounded by an ocean were the whole earth; and the Zuni Indians thought their first ancestors had settled on the Middle Land.

In order to appreciate these stories, one needs to try to put himself imaginatively into these different small worlds. In what kind of country and climate did the people live? How did they keep alive? What kinds of animals and birds did they know? What dangers did they have to face? What sort of picture had they made in their minds of the shape of the earth and sky? What experiences were starting them to wonder and question how things began?

Each story is different from any of the others, yet there are some important ways in which they are alike. Why is this? What are the questions which are not yet fully answered? Twenty-five years from now, when the scientists will probably know much more than they do now, we wonder how their story will be changed. Like Kofi in Africa, we must "go on thinking and thinking and never stop."

SOPHIA L. FAHS

A bushman family in the Kalahari Desert, South Africa.

Story from the Bushmen of Africa

Only a few thousand Bushmen are left in the world today, and most of these now live in the Kalahari Desert in the central part of southern Africa. Once upon a time these Bushmen were perhaps the first people to live in Africa, and they probably spread themselves over many parts of that great continent. Some think that they are descendants of the first cave dwellers in Spain and southern France who during the last Ice Age migrated into a warmer land.

During all these centuries the Bushmen have changed their ways of living very little. They still sleep in caves or find shelter in the simplest of huts made of stacked-up branches. They find their food by trapping or hunting animals with long throwing-sticks and with bows and arrows. The women gather roots and insects and wild berries to add to their diet.

The Bushmen are small people, being often no taller than a twelve-year-old boy. They speak a language that sounds to a stranger like a series of clicks made by striking the tongue against the cheek or the roof of the mouth.

Even though so wild and primitive, some of these Bushmen long ago became remarkable artists. They discovered how to make paints out of different colored clays, and many of their paintings have been found on rock cliffs, and on the walls of caves. Even after thousands of years, the colors are often bright, rich reds, yellowish browns and white. The samples copied in this book suggest the remarkable liveliness and grace of these human and animal figures.

These Bushmen not only believe that animals and growing trees and plants are alive, but to them the rain, the thunder, the wind, bubbling springs, and rivers seem alive also. They say: "What we see is only the outside form or body. Inside is a living spirit that we cannot see. These spirits can fly out of one body into another. For example, a woman's spirit might sometime fly into a leopard; or a man's spirit fly into a lion's body."

A rock painting done by African Bushmen many centuries ago.

In one of their old stories the Bushmen tell how the first people who ever lived used to stand out in the dark at night and look up at the stars and the moon and cry out, "Who made you that you stand so high over the trees? Who are you? Did you make everything?" But the moon and the stars so high up could not hear them shouting. They did not answer.

The story that follows is one among several the Bushmen tell to explain the beginning of life on the earth.

7

The Tree with Animal Fruit

Before there were any people or animals *on* the earth, there were people and animals living *under* the earth with Kaang (Käng) — the Great Master and Lord of All Life. This was a pleasant and happy place where there was no need for the sun, for it was already light, and no one needed to eat anything, for people were never hungry or sick and never died.

Then in that far-off time, Kaang, the Creator, began to plan for the wonders he would make on the earth and above it. First he made a wondrous tree grow out of the earth. It grew and grew until its branches spread high and wide over the country. Near its roots, Kaang dug a hole in the ground. So deep did he make the hole that it reached all the way down to the secret underworld where the animals and people were then living.

When the hole was finished, Kaang called the first man-of-all-men to climb up the hole beside the great tree to the top of the earth. When this first man-of-all-men came out of the top of the hole, he was very much surprised at what he saw. He looked around this way and that way, before him and behind. He looked up at the blue sky high above and saw the big bright sun shining on him through the branches of the great tree. Then the first man-of-all-men sat down on the ground under the tree.

Next Kaang sent up through the deep hole to the top of

All sorts of animals came forth.

the earth the first woman-of-all-women. When she stepped out on top of the earth she was very much surprised at what she saw. She looked around this way and that way, before her and behind. She looked up at the blue sky above her and saw the big bright sun shining on her through the branches of the great tree. Then the first woman-of-all-women sat down on the ground under the tree beside the man.

Soon another man stepped out of the big hole and another woman — then more and more men and women — very many of them. They were all surprised. And they all sat down together under the great tree.

Kaang then began helping the *animals* climb up the hole and out onto the top of the earth beside the great tree. All sorts of animals came, two by two and then three by three, and then four by four. They came — faster and faster — so eager to reach the top that they pushed and squeezed each other through the hole. Finally, some of them in their hurry found a way to push themselves up through the inside of the trunk of the tree, and then out onto the limbs and to the tips of the branches from where they tumbled to the ground.

When the last of the animals had finished coming out of the tree, they all gathered around the people sitting on the grass in the shade. The first animals and the first people began talking to one another, for in the beginning of days, animals and men were friends and could understand each other's language.

While they were sitting talking together, Kaang, their Creator and Master, appeared before them and spoke: "I have brought you out on top of the world together, you and the animals, and I want you to live happily with one another.

Do as I have taught you and be good to one another. There is but one thing no man or woman must ever do. You must never build a fire, for on the day you build a fire, an evil thing will happen to you."

When Kaang had spoken, he disappeared and hid himself somewhere up in the sky where he could keep watch over his creatures. Some say Kaang comes and goes — sometimes he is above in the sky, sometimes below under the earth. But no one ever sees Kaang.

On that first long day, Kaang began planning a new thing for the world. He would make the sun move across the sky and then hide a while under the earth, so that as long as men could see the sun there would be light, but when the sun went down under the earth there would be darkness. So it has always been since that day when Kaang brought the first men and animals up from under the earth. Night regularly follows day.

But on that first day of all days, the first people and the first animals were not expecting the dark to come. As they watched the sun's bright ball moving toward the west and slowly drop lower and lower in the sky, they soon found themselves in darkness. The air grew cool. Men and women, not having furry skins like the animals, began to shiver. They walked about trying to keep warm, but the winds chilled them. The darkness became blacker. They could not see one another or the animals sleeping around them. They began to be afraid.

Finally, one of the men dared to speak up. "Let us build a fire. Surely it is better to be warm than cold. It is better to have light than to try to live in the dark."

So the first man-of-all-men tried to build a fire. He rubbed two sticks together till they grew hot and a red glowing spot appeared. He fed the burning spot with leaves and sticks till flames shot up into the darkness. The first men and women of the world were surprised and filled with wonder. Soon they felt warm again. They could see each other's faces. They were very happy.

But the animals were frightened. They sprang to their feet and rushed off toward the hills. They never came back to sit again under the big tree with the first men and women or to sleep near them. On that night men lost their ability to understand the language of animals, and animals lost their power to talk to men. When men and animals could no longer understand one another, they began to be afraid of each other and unfriendly. Ever since that night when the first man-of-all-men forgot the command of Kaang, his Creator and Master of Life, and built a fire, animals have never been friendly with men except a few, such as the dog and the horse that man has tried to tame.

Australian Aborigines are skilled in throwing their long spears.

Story from the
Australian Aborigines

No one knows how old this story is of "The First Sunrise and Sunset," for no one knows how many thousands of years ago people began living in Australia. When Englishmen first came there to live, a couple of hundred years ago, these primitive Australians had been living all over the con-

tinent. There were probably several hundred thousand of them then. But the English immigrants treated the original Australians much as the early settlers in America treated the American Indians. They drove them from their ancestral hunting grounds and pushed them back into the desert lands of Central Australia, where they have tried ever since to eke out a living on smaller and smaller stretches of country.

These first Australian aborigines are not Negroes although they are often called "black fellows." It is thought that they came originally into Australia from India. Their skin is brown and their hair is usually black, seldom curly. They are often tall and very graceful.

Many of them even today are still wandering hunters who do no planting or gardening. They make no pottery, but the women weave baskets out of reeds, and grasses, and the fiber of barks; some of them are woven so tightly that they will hold water. The men kill their animal game with clubs and boomerangs or with long wooden throwing-sticks tipped with flint arrowheads. They cook their kangaroos whole over hot coals in holes in the ground and cut the flesh with flint knives. The women gather wild roots, grass seeds, berries, and even the pupae of ants to add to their diet. Most Australian aborigines wear no clothes except a simple loincloth. They have no alphabet or written language. What each aborigine knows he learns by word of mouth or by watching and listening to his elders and by trying things out for himself. Yet these primitive hunters know a great deal. They have learned to distinguish between the berries and the roots

A present-day Aborigine paints a picture of one of the spirits to whom he prays.

that are good for them and those that are poisonous. They are able to find hidden water holes and springs in desert wastes where it almost never rains. They can stalk and out-wit the jumping kangaroo. They can spear fish from floating rafts and throw their arrows with a sure aim. They know each animal's footprints and can imitate animal calls and bird songs. They can climb trees whose unbranched trunks reach thirty feet upward. Without books, they have their own songs, their own festival dances and dramas, their own ways of praying, and their own ideas of right and wrong.

These Australian aborigines believe that every living thing — person or animal, even every tree and star and stone — has a living spirit in it. These invisible spirits, they believe, never really die. They simply move from one form of body to another. All the spirits together belong in one great big world family. No Australian aborigine ever feels really alone. He believes he is surrounded by the spirits even though he does not see them. They are his relatives, and one or more greater spirits are always near to guide and to guard the person who tries to listen and obey.

A good old woman, named Kardinnilla — Laughing Stream — often used to tell this story of "The First Sunrise and Sunset." She believed that it was altogether true, and that it had been first told by one of her great great ancestors. Every year in the spring her people used to pantomime the story, singing and dancing and acting out its different parts. And they would paint their naked bodies with colored paint-ings of the birds and reptiles and animals in the story.

The First Sunrise and Sunset

In the far-off time of the long, long ago, the spirits in all living things were fast asleep, dreaming through the world's first long night. Darkness filled all the earth and sky. No insects or animals or people moved about on the earth. No birds flew through the air. No grasses or trees brightened the cold, brown rocks. No streams or rivers flowed through the dry valleys. All was still. Not a sound could be heard. Nothing moved — not even a breeze ruffled the air or made waves in the oceans. The spirits of all living things were lying asleep in the darkness like seeds resting in the earth, waiting for their time. Even the great Sun Mother herself lay in the sky with her eyes of light closed.

Only the Father of All Spirits was awake. How long this first night was no one knows, but at last the Father of All Spirits whispered to the sleeping Sun Mother, "Awake, my Daughter. You have slept long enough."

The Sun Mother drew a long deep breath and when she did so the air around her quivered softly. She opened her eyes, and a bright light beamed from her face into the darkness. She looked into the face of the Father of All Spirits. "What is it, Great Father?" she asked. "I am ready to do as you command." When she had spoken she looked down through the sunbeams that spread about her, and saw the earth below all bare and empty with no grass or flowers or trees.

"Go down to the earth, my Daughter," said the Father of All Spirits. "Wake the spirits that lie in the earth, under the rocks and in the dark caves. Bring them to life. Cover the earth with grasses and flowers and trees. Bring to birth insects, and fish and reptiles and all kinds of birds and animals."

The great Sun Mother flew down to the earth. Swifter than a meteor she flew. When she touched the earth she lighted gently on a great wide plain. At once her warm beams felt pleasant to the cold ground.

Presently she set out to explore the world. First she walked westward. Wherever she stepped, grasses and shrubs and even trees began to spring up in her footprints. On and on she went until she found herself back again in the east where she had started. She then turned northward and walked and walked — on and on — until she found herself back again on the same wide plain from which she had started. And again wherever she stepped grasses and shrubs and even trees began to grow. The Sun Mother walked to the south and back. She walked round and round the earth again and again until it was all covered with green growing grasses, shrubs, and trees.

When the Sun Mother had finished all her walking, she sat down on the plain and rested. She felt pleased with the changes she had made. Then the Sun Mother heard another whisper in her ear. "Go forth, my Daughter, again. Go now into the dark caves on the mountainsides and waken the sleeping spirits there."

So the Sun Mother arose and found her way into a large dark cave. As she entered she brought with her light and warmth. The sleeping spirits were startled. "Why have you disturbed us, O Mother?" they cried. But the Sun Mother did not listen to them. She walked farther and farther into the cave, exploring every corner. When at last she came up out of the darkness, she waited for a short while near the entrance. Presently swarms of insects — ants and beetles — came crawling out of the cave, while butterflies and bees and other flying insects buzzed and flitted about from bush to bush making the valley glow with beautiful colors.

The Sun Mother then returned to the great wide plain and rested. It was a joy to her to watch the grasses and trees and the many colored insects growing together peacefully. Occasionally she would fly to the top of some high mountain and look out over the fields and hills and valleys, or the wind spirits would blow her here and there and show her the bright colors she had brought to the earth.

Still more work was waiting for our Sun Mother to do. Down into another cave she went — one that was deeper and darker and larger than the first cave. Down, down into the darkness she stepped. The ice on the cold rocks melted under her feet. Her shining face spread sunbeams through the darkness of the cave. Wherever she stepped, the spirits of living creatures awoke and began to grow. And when she had finished and walked out of the cave, many small snakes and lizards, frogs and tortoises crept out into the light. And a river flowed out of the mouth of the cave, with fish of many kinds swimming in it.

The Sun Mother returned to the wide grassy plain and rested. Then she set forth again to another cave where living creatures were still dreaming in their sleep. As she stepped down, down, deeper and deeper, into the earth, she found all along the ledges of the rocks and down at the very bottom of the cavern the spirit forms of many kinds of birds — crows, pelicans, ducks, plovers, swans, woodpeckers, magpies, cockatoos, and countless others. She found also the spirit forms of many kinds of animals — rabbits, opossums, koala bears, kangaroos, emus, porcupines, dogs, cats, and many, many other sleeping animal spirits. All these birds and animals were glad for the light. They looked straight at the Sun Mother's bright face, and when she left the cavern they all followed her.

Again the Sun Mother returned to the grassy plain and rested. The great Father of All Spirits joined her. He was pleased with all the plants and trees, with the insects and the birds, with the reptiles and all the other animals that the Sun Mother had brought to life.

When the Father of All Spirits had gone, the Sun Mother called all her children to come together with her on the grassy plain. There were multitudes of them — beyond all counting. They came from the north and the south, from the east and the west.

The Sun Mother spoke to them. "Listen, my children, to your Mother! I have done as the great Father of All Spirits commanded me. Now my work on the earth is ended. I am going up into the sky where I shall shine down upon you and give you light and warmth. Live together peacefully. Do no harm to one another. Enjoy the earth while you can, for the time will come when your bodies will again fall asleep, and will return to the dust. But your spirits will not die. They will live on without bodies, to dream unseen until they are again awakened and given new bodies. Now I leave you. Farewell."

When the Sun Mother had finished speaking, a strong wind lifted her up and up high into the sky. Slowly she glided westward. As she moved farther and farther to the west, her light began to dim. A gray twilight gathered over the earth, till at last the face of the Sun Mother was completely hidden behind the western hills, and darkness covered the whole earth.

As the insects and birds and reptiles and all the other animals watched their Sun Mother going away, they became frightened. When finally they could see nothing in the great darkness, they thought their Mother had forsaken them entirely. They were afraid to move or even to cry. They did not know they had seen the first sunset. They thought it was the end.

After a long, long time of terrified waiting, however, the earth's animal children saw a soft light begin to glow in the eastern sky. Little by little, it grew brighter until finally the creatures all realized that their Sun Mother had come back. Her smiling face was shining on them.

But they were puzzled and said, "Did we not see our Mother go toward the west? How is it she is now rising in the east?" All the insects and birds and animals stood up in surprise and looked straight in the Sun Mother's face.

She did not stay in the eastern sky, however. She kept on moving slowly westward. The animal children watched her curiously through all the day until her light was again hidden behind the western hills, and the earth was covered with darkness. Not quite so afraid, they all waited through the second long darkness, until once more they saw their Mother's shining face in the eastern sky. After this disappearing and re-appearing had happened again and again, the creatures of the earth learned to expect a time of light and a time of darkness to come regularly. And they felt comfortable.

So the earth's children were no longer afraid. The flowers closed their eyes when darkness fell, and opened them again in the morning. The birds rested on the branches of the trees, and the animals found places to sleep in the dark. When the Sun Mother showed her face again in the morning, there was always a happy excitement. The birds chirped and twittered. The animals grunted and barked and called to their mates.

Thus many days and nights went by. The plants, the trees, the birds, the insects, the reptiles, the fish, and all the big and little animals lived together peacefully. But, alas, after a while some became dissatisfied with themselves and grew jealous of others. Some of the animals who had four good feet and could walk wanted to fly, and they cried because they did not have feathers and wings. The fish grew tired of living always in the water, and they envied the animals who had feet and could run about in the sunshine. The insects and the birds envied the animals who were big and strong and they cried because they had no fur.

Finally, the quarreling among the earth creatures grew unbearable. So the Sun Mother left the sky and came back to the earth once more. Calling together all the creatures to whom she had given life, she said:

"O my children, did I not breathe upon your shapeless spirits and give them life? Have I not shone upon you kindly day by day? Still you are dissatisfied. I have decided to let

The first sunset.

each of you turn yourselves into just the kind of living creature you wish to be. You may some day be sorry for the choices you make, but I now give you the power to change yourselves as you wish." The Sun Mother then left them and returned to the sky.

So the fish and birds, the insects and creeping things, and all the animals began changing themselves into new forms. And what strange animals they became! There were rats that turned into bats, and foxes and fish that made wings for themselves. There were insects that made themselves look like sticks and dry grass. There were giant lizards six feet long that could climb trees and catch birds. There were fish that kept their scales but formed blue tongues in their horny pink jaws and grew legs for creeping on the ground.

There was the spiny anteater that could both burrow deep into the ground and climb a high tree. There was the kangaroo that carried her babies in a skin pouch in her own body and grew a strong tail like a fifth leg for jumping. Last of all was the strange platypus, having a bill like a duck and laying eggs like a bird, yet with teeth for chewing and a tail like a beaver. Two of its feet were webbed like a duck's, and all four feet had claws like a bear, and its babies sucked milk from its breasts.

When the Sun Mother looked down from her home in the sky upon all this strange jumbled-up lot of creatures that had come to be, she was no longer pleased. She feared what the Father of All Spirits might say.

She thought to herself: "I must make new creatures. I must put in them more of my own mind so that they will be superior to all the animals."

So the Sun Mother gave birth to two children — a god and a goddess — both of whom were beautiful like herself. The god was the Morning Star and the goddess was the Moon. To this pair were born in turn two other children. The Sun Mother sent these two grandchildren to the earth to live. They became our human ancestors — the first man and woman.

One day the Sun Mother called these new people to her and said, "You, my children, will not wish to change your forms as the insects and birds and fish and creeping things and other animals did before. You are superior to all these other creatures, and I want you to live together in peace as long as you live upon the earth.

"When the time comes that you die, you will become spirits again. Then you will rise to the sky and you will live as stars forever."

Algonkin Indian villagers gathering and grinding corn, skinning deer, and weaving, while a papoose hangs on the tree branch.

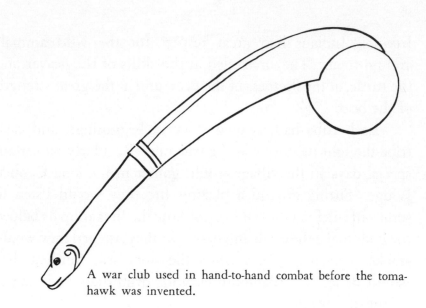

A war club used in hand-to-hand combat before the toma-hawk was invented.

Story from the Iroquois Indians

This story comes from one of the most remarkable of the Indian groups that the first white settlers in North America discovered. The Iroquois lived in sturdily built log houses, supported by strong poles and walled and roofed with strips of bark. They cultivated gardens of corn, beans, and squash. Before white men knew anything about the Iroquois, five of their tribes had formed for their protection what is sometimes called the first League of Nations known in the world, and Hiawatha was their great hero. Rivers, lakes, and towns are still named from these five Iroquois nations — Senecas, Cayugas, Onondagas, Oneidas, and Mohawks. This form of their story of beginnings came from the Wyandots, one of the tribes belonging to the Onondaga nation.

Like most people who live much in the out-of-doors, the

Iroquois Indians had great respect for the wild animals around them. They marveled at the skills of the beaver and the turtle, at the fleetness of the deer, and at the great strength of the bear.

Each tribe had its own story of beginnings, and each tribe thought its story was the true one. Regularly on certain special days all the village would gather in the long Council Lodge. Sitting around a blazing fire they would listen to some old chief tell the old story of how the first animals helped the gods make the earth and man. As they listened they would smoke their pipes; and when the story was finished they would dance it in pantomime, with drummers and singers calling the parts.

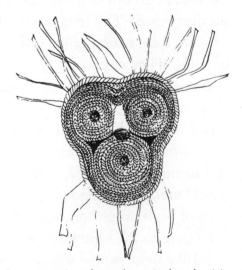

Iroquois husk mask representing the male agricultural spirit.

Iroquois turtle-shell rattle, used as a strength-giving symbol in religious ceremonies.

The First Animals and Twin Gods

In the long, long ago before there were any Indians or any earth, there was a beautiful land above the roof of the sky where the gods lived.

Below the sky was a wide waste of waters in which lived the first water animals — swans, loons, muskrats, beavers, turtles, and toads — with more amazing powers than animals since that time have ever had.

Once when two swans were swimming on the waters, they heard a thundering noise and looked up. Behold, they saw a Sky Woman falling down through a hole in the sky roof.

"What shall we do with this Sky Woman?" cried one of the swans.

"We must receive her on our backs so that she may not be hurt," answered the other swan.

So the two swans drew their two backs close together and the Sky Woman fell upon them.

"Now what shall we do with this Sky Woman?" asked one of the swans. "We cannot forever hold her up."

"We must call a meeting of all the water animals," said the other swan.

So the swans called all the water animals together to decide what they might do.

Big Turtle said, "If someone will dive down into the water and bring up some earth from below, I will hold the earth on my back and we shall then have land for the Sky Woman to live on."

So the water animals took turns in diving. First the muskrat tried. When he came up, Big Turtle looked into his mouth but could find no earth at all.

Then the beaver made a deep dive and came up. He, too, had no earth in his mouth. Others of the water animals tried, but none succeeded in bringing up any earth.

Finally, Little Toad tried. He stayed under the water so long that the other animals thought he would never come up. When at last he did come up out of the water, his mouth was full of earth. Then the animals took the earth from Little Toad's mouth and spread it all over Big Turtle's back.

When they had done this, a strange thing happened. The amount of earth began to grow larger and larger until Big Turtle was holding a whole island on his back. Then the swans swam over to the island and let the Sky Woman step on it, and she started to make it her home.

The island continued to grow larger and larger until it became as large as all of North America, and the back of Big Turtle also grew so that it could hold the island. Sometimes, they say, Big Turtle grows weary of his great load and moves

Big turtle was holding a whole island on his back.

his back to shift the weight. Then the earth shakes. The Indians cry: "Big Turtle is moving."

Now in the beginning when this island earth was young, there were no lights in the sky. The Sky Woman had a hard time finding her way about in the darkness. So the water animals again met in council to decide what they might do about some light for the Sky Woman.

Little Turtle said, "Let me go up to the sky. I will put a light there for the Sky Woman."

Then a great black cloud full of thunder and lightning rolled over the face of the waters. Little Turtle jumped into the cloud and rode up to the sky. He snatched some of the lightning out of the cloud and rolled it into a round ball and fastened it to the roof of the sky. In this way Little Turtle made the sun in the sky.

Since the sun was fastened to one particular spot in the sky and could not move, its light shone constantly on the island earth till it was hot and dry as a desert. Finally the Sky Woman complained of the great heat.

Again the water animals met in council to decide what they might do. After much talk, they decided that the sun should be loosened from the sky and given life so that it could move.

Again Little Turtle rode up to the sky on a big black cloud, and he put life into the sun so that it could move across the sky. Little Turtle also bored a long passageway through under the earth so that the sun might pass underground from one side of the earth to the other. Thus while the sun was passing under the earth, there was darkness above the earth, and only when the sun was up in the sky was the earth light.

So the Sky Woman had a night for resting and a day for working.

Little Turtle made the moon also as a wife for the sun. He put her in the sky to give a soft light to the earth while the sun was going through the underground passageway at night. The sun and moon had many, many children born to them — all the little stars that twinkle at night are their children.

When the earth and the sun, moon and stars had been made, the Sky Woman gave birth to twin boys — not just earth boys but sky boys with the powers of gods in them.

From their first birthdays, these twin boys were not at all alike, one brother being good-minded and the other brother evil-minded. Each brother set out to prepare in his own way the great island earth for human folk to live on.

Good Brother made beautiful woodlands with clear springs and soft flowing rivers. Evil Brother made steep rocky cliffs, with thorn bushes and brambles.

Good Brother made blue lakes and flower-covered valleys. Evil Brother made swamps and dry sandy deserts.

Good Brother made soft summer breezes and spring rains. Evil Brother made cold wintry blasts and hurricanes.

Good Brother made all kinds of trees with fruits growing on low branches easy to reach. He also made blackberries, raspberries, and strawberries grow on bushes without thorns. He made the maple tree drip easily with sweet clear sap. Evil Brother spoiled the fruit on the trees by making them bitter. He dwarfed the bushes and made thorns grow on them and put many seeds into the berries.

Good Brother made the corn and the squash and the

bean grow on high trees. Evil Brother shriveled the ears of corn and the bean pods and made the squash crawl on the ground.

Good Brother made animals that are now useful to men — such as the horse, the buffalo, the eagle, the partridge, and the turkey. Evil Brother made poisonous snakes and dangerous giant mosquitoes. He made bears, panthers, wolves, and monstrous toads that could drink up whole lakes full of water.

So for many long ages these twin gods worked to furnish the earth, Evil Brother continually undoing the work which Good Brother would do.

Had Good Brother been able to work alone mankind would not have known ugliness or hunger, hard labor or pain — only beauty and contentment.

Finally the time came when the two brothers decided to fight till one or the other was conquered. For many hours they struggled, neither one seeming stronger than the other, but at last Good Brother won. Evil Brother was conquered, but being a god he could not die. Instead he was obliged to go down to live underneath the earth on the back of Big Turtle where he could no longer destroy the work of his Good Brother. Only occasionally do men feel his anger in the bursting of a volcano or in the rumbling of an earthquake.

Sosano-wo blowing a storm over the ocean.

Story from the People of Japan

The Japanese people have lived for centuries on eight rather small islands clustered off the eastern shore of China. Until about three hundred years ago they knew little about the other peoples of the world.

Imagine yourself living all your life on an island far out at sea. Suppose that only the bravest and the strongest of your tribe had ever ventured in small boats out on the fearsome ocean to explore the world. Imagine yourself, on their return from these adventures, listening to their tales of wonder.

If you have ever been out on the ocean somewhere and have watched a sunrise or a sunset you will know why the Japanese for many centuries have felt so much reverence for the sun. Surely if you were to imagine a fitting dwelling place for the greatest and the most beautiful of the gods, you could think of none more glorious than in the rainbow-colored skies at sunrise or at sunset!

This story, "From the Floating Bridge of Heaven," may still be read in two very old Japanese books. The oldest is *Kojiki* or *The Record of Ancient Matters* and was written in 620 A.D. The second old book, written one hundred years later, is called *Nihongi* and is more interestingly written than the first.

From the Floating Bridge of Heaven

In the far-off beginning, the air and the earth, the land and the water were mixed up together as the white and yolk of an egg are scrambled for cooking. Within this scrambled world-egg was a germ of life, which grew slowly through the ages and caused the great mass to stir, till at last the clearer part of the great egg rose above the heavier part and became the sky. The heavier part settled down and was like a slimy muddy ocean.

Up in the sky there appeared fleecy clouds; and a rainbow bridge of misty-colored light stretched from the sky down toward the heavier ocean of mud. From out the muddy ocean there appeared a green sprout. It grew higher and higher until it reached the fleecy clouds.

Then the green shoot wished a big wish. It wished to change into a god, and behold, the great wonder came to pass — the tall green stalk changed into a god.

But the new god felt lonely. He wished for other gods. So he made other gods to keep him company. He made a great many gods and they all lived together on the fleecy clouds.

The best of all these many gods were the last two gods to be born. One was Izanagi (I-zä-nä'-gē) — a boy god; and the other was Izanami (I-zä-nä'-mē) — a girl god.

One time Izanagi and Izanami were walking together along the Floating Bridge of Heaven. Looking down below,

they began wondering what there was beneath them. So Izanagi, taking his jeweled staff, thrust it down deep into the muddy ocean below and stirred the waters. As he lifted his staff above the water some lumps of earth stuck to it and fell in drops upon the water. As they touched the surface, these drops began to harden as the white of an egg hardens when it is cooked. Then they grew in size and became the first land upon the earth — one of the islands of Japan.

Izanagi and Izanami stepped down from the Floating Bridge of Heaven upon this island which Izanagi had made. They started to walk around the island, going in opposite directions to explore it. When they met again on the other side of the island, they were glad to see each other. Izanagi said: "What joy beyond compare to see a maid so fair!"

So Izanagi and Izanami fell in love with each other and became man and wife.

Then the two of them together made even more wonders come to pass. They made other islands rise out of the muddy waters. Eight large islands they created. They made also grasses, bushes, brooks, rivers, lakes, and mountains. They covered the hills with forests; they placed snow upon the tops of the mountains and made flowers grow on the plains.

Then Izanagi and Izanami looked out over the beautiful floating islands which they had made and said: "We have made the beautiful eight-island country with its valleys and rivers, forests and mountains. Why should we not produce sons and daughters to rule over these lands!"

Because they were gods, their wishing came true. Their first child was an extremely beautiful daughter whom they

Izanami and Izanagi creating an island out of sea water.

The gods light a bonfire before the cave in which Amaterasu is hiding.

named Amaterasu (Ä-mä-ter-ä´-sū) — Heavenly Light — because her face shone with a glorious brightness.

"She is too beautiful to remain on these islands. Her light should be kept where she can shine on all the children who may be born upon these islands," thought Izanagi and

The gods entice Amaterasu with a merry dance.

Izanami. So they sent their first daughter up the ladder that reached high in the sky, and placed her high above the earth where as the Sun Goddess her light still shines on the children of men.

Their next child was also a beautiful daughter whose

light was of a soft silvery kind — not so dazzling yet still most beautiful. They called this daughter Tsuki-yumi (Sōo-kē-yū′-mē). Izanagi and Izanami sent Tsuki-yumi also up the ladder into the sky, and there as the Moon Goddess she still shines on the children of men.

Amaterasu and Tsuki-yumi, however, soon quarreled. Amaterasu being the older and stronger said to her sister: "You are not a good goddess. I must never again look on your face." So the Sun Goddess and the Moon Goddess have been separated ever since, the Moon Goddess shining in the sky only at night and the Sun Goddess shining only in the daytime.

The third child born to Izanagi and Izanami was a son whom they named Sosano-wo (Sō-sä-nō′-wō). This new child grew to be a very stormy god, mischievous and hot tempered. His face was dark and gloomy. Izanagi and Izanami, fearing that Sosano-wo might do much damage on the beautiful islands they had made, commanded him to stay always on the ocean.

But Sosano-wo was unruly. When he was angry he would not only blow great storms over the ocean but also come up on land, and with his hot breath blow down the trees of the forests and wither the flowers and rice plants that his sister Amaterasu had made grow by her sunshine.

One day Sosano-wo even ventured up the ladder to the sky to be with his sister, the Sun Goddess. She was sitting in the great weaving hall of the gods up in the sky and was weaving garments out of the rainbow's mist. Sosano-wo climbed up on the roof of the clouds, made a hole in them, and threw a big lump of something down at Amaterasu's feet.

At this Amaterasu was so angry that she determined to hide from her hot-tempered brother. Gathering up her shining robes, she crept down the ladder of heaven to the earth and entered a cave. Rolling a stone before the entrance to the cave, she hid herself from the sight of all the gods.

As a result the earth and the sky became dark and all the gods were very much troubled. They began at once to plan a way by which they might persuade the Sun Goddess to come out of the cave.

So the eight million gods and goddesses on the earth and in the sky gathered before the cave in which Amaterasu was hiding. They brought with them trees and set them up in front of the cave. They hung offerings upon the trees — jewels and swords and pieces of garments.

They brought roosters, that they might crow to tell the goddess it was time to come out from her hiding. They lit a bonfire before the cave. One of the best dancers among them began dancing a very merry dance while others played on harps and drums. The dance was so merry that the eight million gods and goddesses began laughing and skipping, shaking the earth with their noise.

At last the sound of this great merriment made the Sun Goddess curious as she lay hiding alone in the cave. She went to the entrance of the cave. She pulled back the big stone a tiny wee bit and peeped out. No sooner had she done this when one of the powerful gods outside widened the opening and pulled Amaterasu out of the cave by force.

With the help of the other gods he carried her up the ladder into the sky. Again the earth and sky were light. A joyful shout rose from the earth. Never again, since this

The gods build a fire, decorate the trees, and dance.

The Sun Goddess is curious, opens the cave, and the gods pull her out.

long-ago time, has the Sun Goddess left the sky except to rest for a night at a time while her sister, the Moon Goddess, sheds her soft silvery light upon the earth.

As the ages passed, among the children who were born to the great Sun Goddess were many gods and goddesses. One of her sons became a mortal man, the first great ruler of the eight-island empire. From that day to this no other emperor has ever ruled Japan except one who claimed descent from the first son of Amaterasu, the beautiful Goddess of the Sunrise and Sunset.

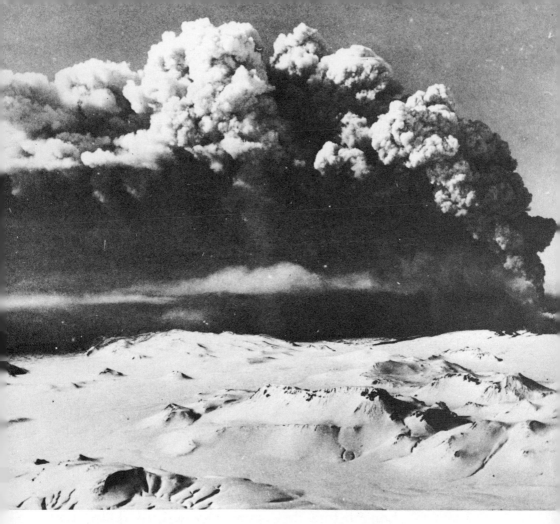

Iceland's great volcano Hekla in eruption.

Story from the People of Iceland

This story of beginnings was probably told by our ancestors in northern Europe a thousand years and more ago. It was told by the Norsemen, who were accustomed to snowy blizzards, and icebergs, and the long half-year night when the sun never rose above the horizon.

Some had perhaps seen their highest mountain turn into a volcano and burst out with flames of fire that must have seemed almost to burn the sky. They had watched the hot lava wind its way slowly down the mountainside, over the white rivers of ice, turning them into sizzling clouds of frost and mist. The burning flames, the piercing winds, and the roaring waves of the ocean seemed to these Norsemen like monstrous giants with wicked hearts.

Then would come the lovely summer to Iceland — the time of wonder and of glowing skies. The big red sun that shone so early in the morning and kept shining till near midnight seemed like the smiling face of a heavenly friend. Green grasses peeped out of the brown earth. Bushes budded and berries ripened. During the glowing nights of these long summers, the people would sit on the sands beside the sea and wonder at the thousands of rainbow-colored streamers of light that stretched far over the wide sky.

This story is part of a very old collection of poems called the *Elder Edda,* meaning the stories of the Elder Grandmothers. Long before they were ever written down, the stories were probably sung or told to circles of listeners huddled around blazing fires in the winter darkness.

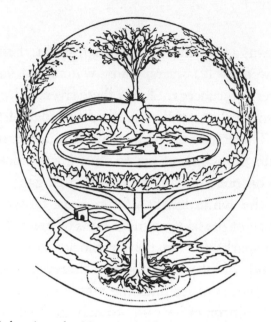

A copy of an old drawing of a Norseman's idea of the universe.

The First Three Things — Ice, Fire, and Salt

When Time began, all was chaos — that is, nothing was formed or in order. "There was neither sea nor sand nor salty wave. There was neither earth nor sky nor green thing anywhere."

In the center of space was a wide, dark, and deep cavern called Gin-nung-ga-gap. On one side of this dark cavern was the place of cold and darkness called Niffl-heim. Huge icebergs, covered with cold mists and frost, rose like mountains. On the other side of the cavern was the place of warmth and light, called Mus-pell-heim. There mountains of fire sent their sparks upward and across the deep dark cavern.

High up on the heights of Niffl-heim, the place of cold

and ice, was a bubbling spring of salt water. From this spring there flowed twelve rivers, whose waters froze as they flowed down over the icebergs. Slowly these rivers of ice moved down and down until at last they reached the edge of the deep dark cavern. There they fell with a hiss and a roaring crash, and broke into thousands of pieces until giant blocks of ice were piled up on one another in Gin-nung-ga-gap.

All the while sparks of fire were blown upward and around, out of the flaming mountains of fire in Mus-pell-heim. As these sparks fell on the icy blocks in Gin-nung-ga-gap, thick clouds of salty mist rose and then fell as snow and rain upon the blocks of ice until the whole deep cavern became a seething cauldron of icy mist. Slowly the blocks of ice became coated with layers of salty frost.

Then, just when no one knows, while the fire and ice were mingling, a wonder came to pass. The salty frost began to come alive. Some of it was gathered up into the shape of a god, and a frosty giant named Ymir slowly rose out of the ice.

Ymir wandered alone up and down over the great ice blocks in search of food. The cold winds from the northland whirled snow and sleet against his face. He could not have seen his way had it not been for the brilliant sparks of fire that were always falling from the hot world to the south.

Ymir, however, was not hungry long, for at the same time that he himself had come alive, there had also been born out of the icy mist a Giant Cow.

Ymir was surprised when he caught sight of the Cow standing near him on the blocks of ice. And he was even more surprised when he saw four streams of milk flowing out from the nipples of her milk bag.

When he had drunk his fill of milk, Ymir lay down on an iceberg and fell asleep. As he slept, three other giants were born from his body. They, too, were strong and terrible, and their hearts were cold as Ymir's heart was cold. So the race of Frost Giants grew in number.

The Giant Cow was also hungry and began licking the great block of ice on which she stood to get the salt that had been frozen within it. She seemed very hungry for she licked and licked the whole day long. At evening there appeared another wonder. From out the ice the Cow was licking, there grew some hairs as if growing on a man's head.

Again the second day the Giant Cow licked the ice block all the day long. And at evening there appeared above the ice not merely a few hairs but the head of a man.

Again a third day the Giant Cow licked the ice and at evening there stood upon the ice a handsome being shaped like a man, but he was more than a man. He was a god, beautiful to look at, and he was different from Ymir because he had a heart that was warm and good. He was called Buri, the first of the Good Gods to live on the earth.

When the giant Ymir saw Buri, he was afraid. He felt in his cold heart that there would be fighting between him and this new god.

After a time Buri had a son and a daughter and then again three grandsons, Odin, Vile, and Ve. So the race of Good Gods grew in number.

As time passed, the Good Gods and the Frost Giants became more and more unfriendly toward each other. Like the fire and the cold ice in Gin-nung-ga-gap, they could not live together in peace in the same place.

Finally, on one of those days before time was counted, the Good Gods and the Frost Giants fought each other in a fierce battle. Odin, Vile, and Ve slew Ymir, and from his body so much blood flowed that all the other Frost Giants were drowned except one and his wife, who escaped.

Then the Good Gods dragged the great body of Ymir, the greatest of the Frost Giants, into Gin-nung-ga-gap. From Ymir's flesh they made the earth. From his great bones they built the mountains. His blood they turned into water to fill the rivers and the great ocean that encircles the earth like a ring. Out of Ymir's small bones, his teeth and jaws, the three Good Gods made pebbles and stones. From his hair grew the thick forests. From his long eyebrows they built a wall of mountains around the earth to keep away the Frost Giants who had escaped.

The three Good Gods then lifted Ymir's great skull above the earth, and from it they formed the dome of the sky. They placed a dwarf at each of the four corners of this dome to hold it up above the earth. In the east was Austre. In the west was Vestre. In the north was Nordre. In the south was Sudre. Ever since, for all time, the sky has been a burden carried by these four dwarfs.

Then the three Good Gods — Odin, Vile, and Ve — caught the red-hot sparks that came falling to the earth from the mountains of fire and rolled them together into balls. They threw them with great might up to the dome of the sky to give light to the earth. The largest of all became the sun. The next in size became the moon. The other sparks became the stars.

Ages passed. The earth became covered with plains and seas and forests, but no human being had yet been born. As the three Good Gods, Odin, Vile, and Ve, were one day walking along together near the sea, they found two fallen trees, one an ash and the other an elm. Immediately, with knives and hatchets, they began shaping the two logs. The ash they shaped like a man and the elm they shaped like a woman. Then Odin breathed life into the two forms and they became living persons. Vile gave them minds for thinking. And Ve gave them eyes for seeing and ears for hearing and tongues for talking. They called the man *Ask* and the woman *Embla*. From these two first persons in the world all the human race has descended.

Above the center of the earth, on a plateau high on a mountain, the three Good Gods then built a large and beautiful city, where they themselves might dwell apart from the people on the earth. They called it *Asgard,* the home of the gods. In the midst of Asgard there grew a giant tree, called Ygg-drass-il (Ig-dräs´-il). Its branches spread high and far over the whole sky, and its roots spread deep and long beneath the earth. Watered by an eternal spring, the leaves of Ygg-drass-il are always green and its fruit is always luscious. Here the gods and goddesses live and work apart from mankind. Yet they can look down upon the earth and watch over the race of men they created.

Over-arching high above the earth, Odin built a bridge of fire, water, and air, which is called Bi-frost, the rainbow, along which the gods may travel down to the earth and back again to Asgard. Although the gods always lived apart from men, yet they have never forgotten the creatures they made.

Odin, the greatest of all the gods, has been called the All-Father for he is not only the Father of all the gods but the Father also of all men and of all living things on the earth. Odin is ever ready to send his helpers to the earth to protect his creatures against the wicked Frost Giants should they break loose from their prison beyond the high mountains that encircle the edge of the earth.

The symbol of the Yang and Yin — the cosmic egg.

Story from the People of China

The people of China have been a civilized and great nation for a longer time than any other great nation now on earth, except perhaps India and Egypt. Learned Chinese scholars wrote books, and Chinese artists produced great

55

paintings and molded beautiful figures and vases in clay and stone and porcelain more than a thousand years ago.

The story that follows is a combining of two ancient Chinese ways of thinking. The first part is the way of the wise men, and the second part is the story that people could remember because it could be put more easily into pictures as well as into words.

Some great artist long ago put the great thought that is in the first part of the story into a drawing. Of course, no one can draw the likeness of a thought, but a picture can suggest the feelings the great thought brings us, and it can suggest a little of what the thought is like. Such a picture we call a symbol. The one shown here is one of the great symbols of the world.

The circle around the picture suggests the feeling the Chinese have when they think of Tao, the Great Original Cause, that lies hidden and around all things. The two curling things, black and white, going round and round are the *Yang* and the *Yin* — the opposite things. And the eight designs around the Yang and the Yin are called the *Eight Trigrams,* meaning the eight designs, each with three parts in it. The longer line means the Yang and the shorter lines mean the Yin. These two marks are combined in a different way in each of the eight designs. So the Yang and the Yin mingle together in different ways at different times and places.

P'an Ku chiseling out the universe with the dragon, the sacred phoenix and the turtle helping.

The sacred phoenix.

Yang and Yin and the Dwarf P'an Ku

Before the beginning of days — before the earth was
formed or the sky — there was *Tao,* the Great Original Cause.
All things came from Tao and on Tao all depend.

Tao reached everywhere. Tao was smaller than the
smallest and greater than the greatest.

In Tao was the power to change all things.

So it came about that Tao brought into being the two great elements, the Yang and the Yin.

Just what the Yang and the Yin are it is hard to explain, for no one can see either one of them.

Whatever they are, they are very important, since from these two powers all else has come.

The Yang and the Yin are the opposites of each other.

The Yang is like man. The Yin is like woman.

The Yang is active. The Yin is at rest.

The Yang is like the day. The Yin is like the night.

The Yang is like the summer. The Yin is like the winter.

The Yang is like the sky. The Yin is like the earth.

The Yang is like a blossoming flower. The Yin is like the fading leaf.

The Yang is like being born. The Yin is like dying.

The Yang is not better than the Yin. Nor is the Yin better than the Yang. They are both good.

So there was in the beginning the Yang and the Yin — each the opposite of the other. As the Yang and the Yin flowed round and round and mingled together, the specks of life in each of them joined and became one life and this new life began to grow. A shell like the shell of an egg formed around it. After ages of time, so long that no one can imagine how long it was, this germ of life grew and grew within the world-egg until it became strong.

Then the sound of hammering inside the great shell began. As a young chick pecks its way through its shell, so P'an Ku, a shaggy dwarf, began breaking his way through the shell of this world-egg. He had two horns on his head. Two tusks bent outward from his bearded jaws. His body was covered with fur like a bear. In his left hand was a hammer. In his right hand he held a chisel.

When P'an Ku had come forth fully from the great egg, he began arranging the Yang and the Yin in many forms. He made the earth thick and flat and floated it on a great expanse of water. He made the sky and lifted it high above the earth. Then with his chisel he began splitting the large rocks upon the earth. He piled them up into high mountains. He hammered down the valleys. He hollowed out the river beds and commanded the water to flow into them. By his breathing P'an Ku made breezes blow across the lands. When he opened his eyes light shone all around.

Day after day P'an Ku worked making the earth and sky. Each day he worked he grew six feet taller than he was the day before, and each day he lifted the sky six feet higher from the earth. P'an Ku worked all the days it takes to make 18,000 years. Some say he worked 800,000 years. So when he had finished, P'an Ku was no longer a dwarf. He had grown to be the tallest of all giants, and the sky was extremely high and the earth had become very large.

Still the wonders grew that P'an Ku brought to pass. He wrote the word "Sun" in the palm of his right hand. He wrote the word "Moon" in the palm of his left hand. He lifted his arms till they touched the high sky.

P'an Ku then called the word "Sun." He called it seven times. And the sun appeared.

He called the word "Moon." He called it seven times. And the moon appeared in the sky. Finally he created all the stars to light the sky at night.

The dragon, the symbol of power and protection.

When at last P'an Ku's work of creating the earth and the sky was finished, he lay down and died.

On his death his head became mountains. His breath became winds and clouds. His voice became the thunder. His blood turned to mighty rivers. His flesh became soil. His skin and hair became plants and trees. His teeth and bones became metals and rocks and precious stones. His sweat became rain. The insects crawling over his body changed into human beings. These human beings grew in size and multiplied in number, for they learned to love and to have babies. Slowly, very slowly, as the centuries passed, they became cleverer and cleverer.

And all the while the Yang and the Yin, with which Tao, the Great Original Cause, began, was in them and in all things everywhere. These opposites have been mingling and helping each other — the male and the female, the light and the dark, the heat and the cold, day and night. The Yang and the Yin are both good.

Story from the Sumerians and Babylonians

This very old story has only recently been discovered. It was first written in the oldest known written language in the world, the Sumerian language. Fifty years ago, no one had ever heard of the Sumerians. Now it is thought they were the most remarkable people of the ancient world. They were the first people to learn how to drain large stretches of marsh and cultivate wheat on the rescued land. They were the first people to build large walled cities, with two-story houses and majestic temples. The Sumerians were the first people to invent a written language and the first to have schools, where not only their boys but also their girls could learn to read and write and do arithmetic problems.

How were the Sumerians discovered? First by discovering the very old libraries of the Babylonian kings who conquered the Sumerians and used the Sumerian language and writing, and copied many of the Sumerian stories of their gods and kings.

Only a few years ago some men from the British Museum of London were digging in the ruins of the ancient famous city of Nineveh when they came upon a room in the king's palace which was piled high with thousands of books — accidentally buried and forgotten twenty-five hundred years before! Some of these books were perhaps already a thousand

A statue of a Sumerian gentleman who lived some four thousand years ago.

years old when the palace was destroyed. And the books were written in a language those British scholars could not read — a language they had never seen the like of before.

"Weren't the books moldy after being buried in the damp earth for over two thousand years?" you ask perhaps. Not at all, but some were broken; for the books in this library were all made of baked clay. They were in size and shape somewhat like a shredded wheat biscuit. When each clay book was soft, its writer had made marks in the clay with a small stick, having a point shaped like a triangle. Each little group of straight lines he made in the clay stood for a word or a sound. When the writing was finished, the clay tablet was baked in the sun and later put away on a shelf to keep.

Professors had been finding clay tablets with such writing on them in many ruined cities of the Middle East. They gave the name *cuneiform* (kū-nē'-i-form) to the writing. Later they found it was the very old language of the Sumerians, but no one could read it. A few men in Britain and America had to be very persevering and clever, else they would never have figured out how to read this very odd writing.

This special story that follows was written on seven clay tablets, called *The Seven Tablets of Creation*. Most of one of these tablets is still missing. The story is Sumerian but retold by Babylonians with a few changes to fit it to them. We have Dr. E. A. Speiser of the University of Pennsylvania to thank for his very fine translation of the story into English, which we have shortened for this book.

A Sumerian tablet recording part of the stories of The Creation and The Flood.

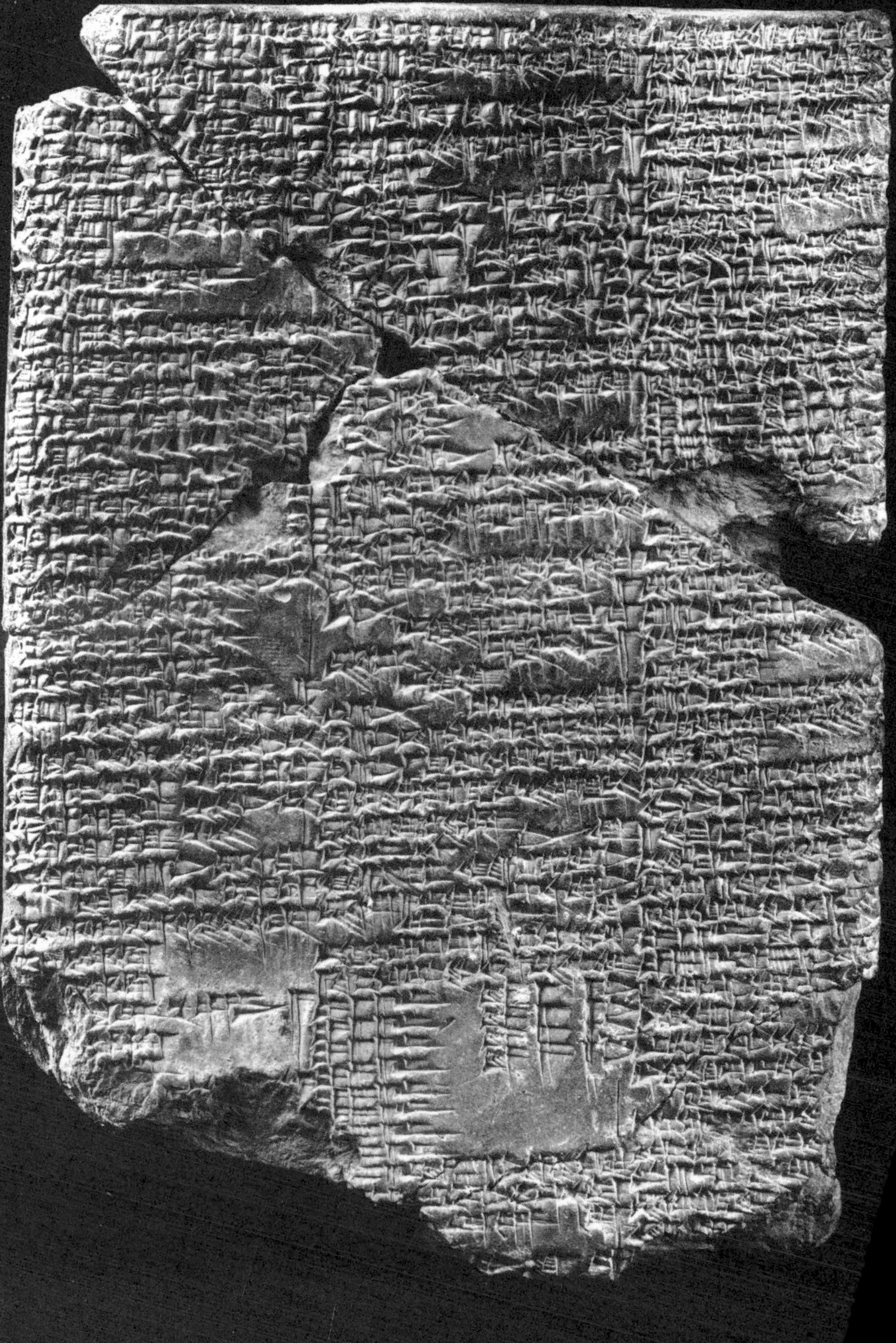

For many hundreds of years, on the fourth day of the New Year's Festival, the high priest in the great temple of Babylon used to chant this poem of creation. Probably parts of it were dramatized and danced in the open court where the people could watch and listen.

The Gods in Battle Before Creation

When above no heaven had been created,
And below no earth had yet appeared,
Nothing had been separated from anything else.
Apsu, the spirit of fresh water, and Tiamat, the spirit of salt
    water, moved quietly within the watery deep,
Apsu and Tiamat, the First Father and First Mother of all
    that is.

Unmeasured time passed by.
Other gods were born — male and female — they came forth.
In turn they too had children, and their children gave birth to
    grandchildren.
Even great grandchildren added to the number of the gods.
But each generation of gods grew taller than its parents.
Sons became wiser than their fathers, and grandsons grew
    grew taller than their grandfathers.
The younger gods could do things their parents had never
    tried to do.

Marduk and Tiamat in Battle.

They were not so peaceful or quiet as the First Parents.
Their noisy laughter and their running about here and there
   disturbed Apsu.
He tried to lessen his children's clamor but could not.
Tiamat loathed her children's behavior,
But she said not a word.

Finally Apsu could no longer endure the confusion.
He called Mummu, his counselor; "Go with me to Tiamat.
Let us talk things over with her."

So Apsu and Mummu sat down before Tiamat. Apsu let loose
his complaint.

"I detest the way our children behave. I have no quiet during
the day and I can not sleep at night. Let us destroy our bois-
terous children. I must have rest."

But Tiamat hated the thought. "What?" she cried out angrily.

"Shall we kill those whom we ourselves have created? I know
their ways are troublesome, but let us deal kindly with
them."

Apsu could say no more. But Mummu, his counselor, urged
him on.

"Your plan, my Lord, is the right one. You must be rid of
your troublesome children. Only then can you have rest
from their clamor."

Then Apsu's face glowed. He threw his arms around Mummu's neck.

He sat him on his knees and kissed him.

They walked away together to plan their cruel work.

News of Apsu's plot spread quickly among the gods.

They were dismayed; they sat a long while in silence.

Finally, Ea, the wisest among them and the most skilled in
magic, spoke.

Ea alone had the boldness to act against his great grandfather
Apsu.

He made a magic spell, a powerful one.

He recited the words of the spell over the deep waters.

He poured sleep over Apsu, till the First Father was drenched
in sleep.

Ea removed his head band, tore off his crown and put them on
  himself.
He bound Apsu with ropes and then he slew him.
He bound Mummu also and left him to die.

Then Ea, the conqueror, built his dwelling place on the giant
  body of Apsu.
There he and his wife Damkina lived in splendor and quiet.
In time a son was born to them, Marduk, the perfect one,
  destined to be the tallest, the most awesome and the strong-
  est of all the gods.
Marduk with the four eyes and four ears,
Marduk who can see and hear all things.

Others of the gods, however, were angered when they heard
  how Ea had slain their First Father.
Kingu, Tiamat's favorite son, led the rebellious group.
They went to their First Mother. They told her of Apsu's
  murder.
"You do not love us if you simply sit in silence and do nothing.
  For our sakes you must take revenge on our Father's mur-
  derer."

Tiamat was stirred by her children's pleading.
She determined to have revenge.
She summoned the rebellious ones to her side.
They plotted night and day.
They growled and raged and prepared for the battle.
Tiamat called Kingu before her. "I now make you our com-
  mander in chief."

She fastened the Tablets of Fate on his breast. "I am casting
a spell over you. I am giving you the power to make this
rebellion succeed."

The Great Mother then created new and living weapons for
her army.
She created monster snakes with sharp teeth, roaring dragons
with poisonous fangs and dazzling heads.
She created giant lions and dogs and scorpions and giant
dragon flies and centaurs.

When Ea, in his pleasant dwelling, heard of Tiamat's angry
plot, he lapsed into gloomy silence.
For a very long while he brooded.
At last when his anger cooled, he went to his father Anshar
for advice.
"Tiamat is in a furious rage. Our Mother who bore us now
detests us. Many of the younger gods have rallied to her
side. They have formed an army. They are marching
against us."
Anshar pounded his thighs.
He covered his mouth to stifle an outcry.
When he regained his mind, he spoke.
"Ea, my son, you have slain Apsu and Mummu. You are
brave and strong. Go now yourself and stand before Tiamat. Do not slay her but try to calm her mood. Tell her
we still honor her as our First Mother."

Part of the Fourth Babylonian Tablet of Creation.

Bravely Ea went forth at once to find Tiamat. But when he
came near enough to see her, he was frightened by the sight
of her.

His courage failed him. He turned back.

He was ashamed to face his father Anshar. He felt small.

He confessed, "I am not able to face Tiamat."

Anshar frowned and shook his head at Ea.

He and the company of gods with him all sat in gloomy silence.

They were of one mind. "No one is able to go to battle against
Tiamat."

But Anshar would not give up hope. His eyes darkened.

He said nothing. But he continued to ponder.

"Surely there must be some one stronger than Tiamat," he
said. "Who can it be?"

No one spoke. Anshar knew there was only one who could
be trusted with the dangerous venture.

Ea's favorite son, the lordly Marduk, the pride of his father's
heart.

Would Ea be willing to let his son go?

Anshar called Marduk to his side. "Your father Ea tried to
face Tiamat but found his arms too weak to pull the bow.
Tell us, O Marduk, will you go?"

Marduk accepted Anshar's proposal. "Sit no longer in silence
and gloom, grandfather. I will go and carry out your desire.
Who is it that is pressing the fight against us anyway? Is
it not merely a woman? Why should I be afraid?"

The gloom on Anshar's face faded away.

He kissed Marduk's lips. "Go then to Tiamat. But do not slay
her. Merely calm her with one of your powerful spells."

"Grandfather, I will go," said Marduk, "I will destroy Tiamat.
But I will do it on one condition only, that you give me the
supreme power. You must proclaim to all that from this
time on Marduk is king."

Such an important decision must be made by the gods together.

Anshar could not do it alone. Ea could not do it alone.

Could the gods be persuaded? Ea suggested preparing a banquet.

"Put the gods in a happy and generous mood by tempting
them with food and wine. Then let the vote be taken."

So the gods gathered in their great banquet hall.

As they feasted they forgot their fears. They grew light
hearted and content.

Then Anshar announced Marduk's brave offer. He was their
one hope of success.

He deserved their highest honor. "Let us proclaim him our
supreme ruler."

The gods of heaven shouted their approval.

Marduk was led to the throne chair.

They gave him a sceptre, a mace and a crown.

They bowed before him, saying "Marduk is our King!"

Marduk went forth from the banquet to prepare for the battle
with Tiamat.

He made a new bow and fixed the bow cord.
The arrows he hung in a quiver by his side.
In front of him he set the lightning.
He wove a great net to enfold Tiamat.
He placed the four winds on the four sides of the deep waters
    so that none could escape.
He created the Whirlwind, the Hurricane and the Cyclone.
He stirred the great waters into a storm.
He mounted his storm chariot.
He yoked it to four horses — Killer, Relentless, Trampler and
    Swift.
He turbaned his head with a fearsome cap.
He grasped a healing plant in his hand to ward off poison.
He wrapped himself in a cloak of terror.

Many of the gods followed after him.
As they approached the terrible Tiamat their eyes blurred.
They moved about in circles.
Tiamat cried out with a savage shriek.
Marduk answered with a clear strong challenge. "You have
    proudly stirred up some of your own sons to rebel. You
    detest your own children. You have exalted Kingu who has
    no right to be ruler of the gods. Stand up now before me.
    You and I must meet in single combat."

Tiamat became as one mad.
In her fury she cried out.
Her legs trembled and shook against each other.
She recited a magic spell, but it failed to reach Marduk.

Marduk spread out his net to enfold Tiamat.
He let loose the Whirlwind in her face.
When she opened her mouth he drove the wind into it.
She could not close her mouth again.
Marduk released his arrow and pierced her heart.

Seeing their leader dead, Tiamat's followers turned their backs
   and ran.
Tightly encircled by Marduk's wide net, they could not escape.
He held them ensnared.
Marduk seized Kingu. He bound him.
He took from him the Tablets of Fate and fastened them to his
   own breast.

Marduk turned again to the body of Tiamat.
He slit her body like a shellfish into two parts.
Half he raised on high and set it up as sky.
He made bars to hold it up.
He measured the Heaven above and set it over the sky.
He marked the places for the stars.
He created the sun and moon.
He planned the days and nights, the months and years.
From the lower half of Tiamat's body, Marduk made the
   earth.
Her bones became its rocks.
Her blood its rivers and oceans.

Marduk then returned to Heaven.
Fifty of the great gods gathered in the banquet hall.

Marduk was seated in the place of highest honor.

Ea, his father, displayed the great net that had ensnared the rebels.

He held up Marduk's bow and arrow that had pierced Tiamat's heart.

He kissed it. He praised the skill of its maker.

Marduk spoke to the assembled gods.

He reported all that he had accomplished.

But there was still more to do. "We need creatures to serve us," he said.

"I will create man and woman who must learn to plow and to plant, and make the earth bring forth food and drink for us.

I will make them of clay, but they must have in them the blood of the gods.

Who among us shall be sacrificed? Who was it that contrived the uprising?

Who was it that persuaded Tiamat to rebel?

Let him be brought to me."

Kingu was brought bound before Marduk.

One of his arteries was cut, and from his godly blood mixed with clay Marduk fashioned the first man and woman.

Years passed by. People on the earth learned to till the ground.

They drained the marshes and built walled cities.

They learned to fashion reed huts and mat them with clay.

They learned to make bricks and pile them high one upon another.

In the great city of Babylon they built a temple that rose like a
    mountain toward the sky.

In its chambers the gods were made glad.

The people of the earth brought food and drink to its altars.

Daily they sang praises to Marduk, supreme among the gods;

He who created the vast spaces and fashioned the earth and
    men;

He who both creates and destroys; who is god of storms and
    of light;

He who directs justice; a refuge for those in trouble;

From whom no evil doer can escape;

His wisdom is broad. His heart is wide. His sympathy is
    warm.

Many are Marduk's names.

But in him all gods are one.

A copy of an old drawing of the ancient Hebrews' idea of the universe.

Stories from the Hebrews of Palestine

These two stories, "The First Seven Days of Time" and "The Forbidden Fruit," can be found in the Jewish-Christian Bible in the very first part of the very first book of the Bible — the book of Genesis. Genesis is a Greek word meaning *Beginnings*.

When these stories were first told we cannot say. Abraham and his family probably heard stories quite a little like them when they lived in the land of the Sumerians on the banks of the Euphrates River. The storytellers who repeated the stories and the people who heard them believed that the earth was flat and circular, that it was held firmly in place in some way so that it did not move. They thought of the sky as a great high dome covering the top of the earth, and of the sun, moon, and stars as lights fastened to this dome. As the dome revolved around the earth, the sun, moon, and stars also revolved. Above this dome the people thought there was water. When God opened the windows in the dome some of the water fell to the earth as rain. They imagined God as living above the ocean that was above the dome, yet he could fly down to the earth whenever he chose to do so.

These stories were first written in the Hebrew language. In Hebrew the name for God in the first story is Elohim (E-lō-heem), and the name in the second story is Jahweh (Yä-wāy). Since the English-speaking world has usually used the general name God for both these Hebrew names, we have done so also in retelling the stories. Although the stories were first written by two different men, both of them were thinking of the Creator, who was before the world began and who brought into being all that is.

The first two days of Creation, as pictured in the first Bible printed in English, in the year 1535 A.D.

The First Seven Days of Time

In the beginning God — the All Powerful — the Eternal One — created the heaven and the earth.

The earth was without form and darkness covered the deep waters. And God moved over the deep waters, blowing the wind of his breath into them.

He said: "Let there be light!" and there was light. God looked on the light he had created, and said, "It is good."

Then God separated the light from the darkness. He called the light Day and the darkness he called Night.

And the evening and morning were the first day.

The third and fourth days of Creation.

God spoke again: "Let there rise above the waters a strong arched dome. Let the part of the waters above the arched dome be held separated from the waters under the great arched dome."

And God called the arched dome the Sky.

And the evening and the morning were the second day.

God spoke again: "Let the waters under the sky be gathered together in one place and let dry land appear." And it was so. The dry land became the continents and the waters became the seas.

God looked out over the land and the seas he had created, and said: "They are good."

Again God said: "Let the earth bring forth grass, and let plants come up that have seeds, and let all kinds of fruit trees grow upon the earth, each bearing its own kind of fruit with its own kind of seeds."

The fifth and sixth days of Creation.

And it was so. The earth brought forth grass, plants came up that bore seeds, and all kinds of fruit trees grew, each bearing its own kind of fruit.

God looked over the land and the sea and saw all the growing things and said: "They are good."

And the evening and the morning were the third day.

Then God said: "Let there be lights in the sky to light the earth and to divide the day from the night. Let them mark the days and the seasons and the years." And it was so.

God made the two great lights; the sun, the greater light, to rule by day, and the moon, the lesser light, to rule by night. He made also all the stars and put them into the dome of the sky to give light to the earth.

God looked out at the sun, moon, and stars he had created, and said: "They are good."

And the evening and the morning were the fourth day.

God then said: "Let the oceans swarm with living creatures. Let birds fly above the earth and beneath the great arched dome of the sky."

So God created all the great sea monsters and every kind of fish that swims in the waters and every kind of bird with wings.

He looked out on all the fish and birds he had created, and said: "They are good."

And God blessed all these living creatures and said: "Be happy; have many young and fill the waters and the sky with your life."

And the evening and the morning were the fifth day.

And God said: "Let the earth bring forth other living creatures also — wild beasts, cattle, and animals that crawl on the ground."

So God made every kind of wild beast, and every kind of cattle, and every kind of animal that crawls.

He looked upon these animals he had created, and said: "They are good."

God said: "I will make human beings like myself. Let these human beings rule over all the animals, over the fish in the seas, over the birds in the sky, over the cattle, and over every animal that crawls on the ground. Let men become the rulers over all the earth."

So God created a man and a woman like himself; and he blessed them and said: "Be happy. Have many children. Fill the earth with your people. Rule over the fish of the sea and over the birds of the air and over every other living thing that moves upon the earth."

"I give you for your food all the plants bearing seeds and all the trees bearing fruit everywhere on the earth."

"I give the green plants to the wild beasts, and to the cattle, and to the birds of the air for their food."

And God looked out upon everything that he had made, and said, "It is all very good."

And the evening and the morning were the sixth day.

So the sky and the earth were finished, and all the millions of living creatures, on the earth, in the air, and in the waters. God had created the first man and woman.

So on the seventh day God rested, having completed all the work he had planned.

For this reason God has blessed every seventh day making it a holy day in which men should do no work, but should rest as God himself rested from his work of creation on the first great seventh day of time.

The Forbidden Fruit

In the beginning of days God had completed creating the earth and the sky, the sun and moon, and all the millions of stars, but as yet there were no growing plants or trees on the earth for God had not yet sent any rain to water the ground. And there were no animals of any kind. Nor were there any human beings.

So God made a great mist rise up from the ground until all the earth was moist. Then he took some of the moist earth in his hands and molded it into the shape of a man. When God saw the beautiful form he had made, he breathed into the nostrils of the clay figure his own breath of life and it became a living person, the first man.

Then God caused all kinds of plants and herbs and trees to sprout up out of the ground until he had made a very pleasant garden filled with flowers, bushes, and trees. All the trees that God created were pleasant to look at and bore fruit good for food. And God called the garden Eden. In the center of the garden he planted a special tree with a special name. He called it the Tree of Knowledge of Good and Evil. And God created four rivers and made them flow through the garden.

God then called the man he had made and led him into this pleasant garden, and said to him: "This garden is yours to enjoy and to care for. You may eat freely of the fruit of all the trees in the garden except the fruit of one of them and that one is the Tree of Knowledge of Good and Evil. Of its fruit you must never eat, for on the day that you eat its fruit you will die."

God then left the man alone in the garden. But after a while, as God watched the man walking about the garden with no one to talk to, he felt sorry for Man. "It is not good for Man to be all alone," God said to himself. "I will make some helpers for him."

So God, the Creator, gathered other pieces of moist clay, and molded them into one shape after another until he had made all the kinds of animals and birds and fish that there are now in the world. And God brought these animals one by one to the man for him to name. Whatever name the man gave the animal that is what it is called. But even though man gave a name to every one of the animals, and even though the animals could talk with man in those times when the world was young, still man did not find the animals good helpers to him.

So God, the Creator, made the first man fall into a deep sleep. As he slept God cut out one of the man's ribs, and closed up the skin over the cut. Then out of this rib which God had taken from the man, he made a woman. When God had breathed into her nostrils also the breath of life, she became a living person, the first woman. God then brought the woman to the man. When the man saw her he was pleased and said: "At last here is one whose bones and flesh are like my own. She has truly come from my own body. This woman and I are as one person." And the man and woman loved each other.

Adam and Eve tried to hide among the trees.

Now there was in the garden of Eden a snake that was very clever, more so than any of the other animals that God had made. But this snake was to use his cleverness not for the good of the first man and woman but for their evil.

Meeting the woman one day beside the tree in the center of the garden, the snake said to her: "Did God tell you that you might eat freely of the fruit of all the trees in the garden?"

The woman answered the snake: "We may eat of the fruit of all the trees we wish except this one that is in the center of the garden. God has told us that we must never eat its fruit. We must not even touch the tree for the day we do so we will die."

"You will not die if you eat the fruit of this tree," contradicted the snake. "God knows that when you eat of this fruit you will become wise. Your eyes will be opened and you will be able to know the difference between what is good and what is bad. You will become like God himself when you eat this fruit."

The woman looked up at the tree. Its fruit was indeed a delight to see. She thought, "If this fruit will make me wise why shouldn't I eat it?"

The snake waited and watched. Presently the woman reached up to a branch, picked one of the fruits and began eating it. She picked another fruit and ran with it to the man. She told him what the snake had said, and how delightful the fruit tasted. Then the man took the fruit from her hand and he too ate.

When they had finished eating the fruit the man and woman looked about them. It seemed almost as though their eyes had been shut before and now they were open. Everything looked beautiful. There was a moment of great happiness. Then they began to feel ashamed — ashamed even to be naked; and they started to make aprons out of leaves to cover themselves.

Later in the cool of the afternoon, while they were busy weaving their aprons, they heard the sound of someone walking nearby in the garden. They were afraid for they knew it was God, and they ran and hid themselves among the bushes. "Where are you?" called God.

The man answered: "I heard the sound of your footsteps in the garden and I was afraid and hid myself because I was naked."

"Who told you you were naked?" asked God. "Have you been eating the fruit of the tree I commanded you not to eat?"

"The woman you created gave me one of the fruits and I ate it."

Then God turned to the woman and said: "What is this you have done?"

The woman answered: "The snake tempted me, and I ate."

Then God turned to the snake and said: "Because you have done this, I now curse you. From this day on you and your descendants will always crawl on the ground, and you and women will always be enemies."

To the woman God said: "Because you have done this, you and all women will always have great pain when you give birth to babies, and from this day on husbands will rule their wives and wives will have to obey their husbands."

Then God turned to the man and said: "Because you have done this, because you listened to this woman and because you have eaten of this fruit, I am cursing the earth and all that is in it. From this day on, you and all men after you will have to work hard and long in order to make plants good for food grow in this cursed ground. Thistles and thorns will grow up for you instead except as you labor to weed them out. I intended that you and woman should never die. I meant for you to live forever, but now your punishment must be that you will grow old and die and your bodies will turn back into the lifeless dust out of which I first made you."

God gave the first two people names. He called the first man Adam and the first woman he called Eve.

Then God said: "Now that this first man and this first woman have become wise and know the difference between good and evil, they may try eating the fruit of that other special tree in the center of the garden. They may eat the fruit of the Tree of Life and so live forever and be like gods unless I shut them out of the garden."

So God drove Adam and Eve out of the garden of Eden and closed the entrance gate. He called a tall and frightening angel down from heaven, put into his hand a sword of fire, and stationed him beside the gate so that Adam and Eve could never again enter the garden.

From that day to this all men and women born on the earth have found that life is filled with hardships, pain, and sickness, and in the end everyone must die.

Sometimes the Mayans thought of the Creator as two gods, male and female.

Story from the Maya Indians of Yucatan

This story, written long before the Spaniards came to America, was found carved on the stone over the doorway to the palace in the beautiful capital city of Chitzen Itza.

Later the story was written in an old book called the *Popul Vuh*. *Popul* means in the Maya language a mat woven

A Mayan temple to the Creator
in Chitzen Itza, Yucatan

Often the Mayans thought of the Creator as a great serpent with
quetzal feathers on his head and with a human face and hands.

of grass which was large enough for the whole family to sit
on together. *Vuh* means paper or book. So the *Popul Vuh*
was the book read to all the family as they sat together on the
mat. It might perhaps be called the Family Bible of the Maya
Indians.

Heart-of-the-Earth-and-Sky

In the beginning the face of the land was hidden. There was nothing but the silent sea and the sky. There was nothing joined, nor any sound, nor anything that stirred. Then Heart-of-the-Earth-and-Sky appeared. He passed like a mighty wind over the sleeping waters. He called the earth to come forth, and solid land was there.

Heart-of-the-Earth-and-Sky finished creating the world with its mountains and valleys, its rivers and lakes; but the time of the first sunrise had not yet come. A soft twilight hung over the world. There were neither animals nor men to walk on the earth.

Heart-of-the-Earth-and-Sky made the animals that were to live on the mountains, deer and lions, rabbits and squirrels. To large and small alike he gave life, from tigers to tiny snakes that crawled through the weeds. He made the birds that were to fly in the air, and the fish to swim in the rivers and seas. Finally, he made the tiny creatures, ants and worms, butter-flies and moths.

Heart-of-the-Earth-and-Sky then stood and looked at the creatures to which he had given life.

He called the animals to him, each in his turn. First, he spoke to the deer. "You shall live on the hillsides and in the ravines which lie between them. You shall walk on four feet and run with swiftness. You shall drink from the brooks and gather your food in the forests."

Heart-of-the-Earth-and-Sky called all the other animals to him, each in his turn, and told them also where they were to find their homes and just how they were to live.

To all the animals alike he gave this final direction. "Each of you," he said, "will be able to speak only as the other animals of your kind. Deer shall speak with deer, snake with snake, and rabbit with rabbit. But the deer shall not speak with the rabbit, nor the snake with the deer. Only with animals of your own kind shall you speak."

Still the time for the first sunrise had not yet come. Only a soft twilight hung over the earth.

Heart-of-the-Earth-and-Sky, as he watched the creatures he had made, wished that they might thank him for the things he had done for them. He wished them to show that they were grateful for all his gifts.

So he called the animals together to give thanks to their creator. But when they had gathered, the animals did not know how to speak words of praise. Some could croak while others could bray. Some could bellow while others could bark. But one kind of animal could not understand another kind of animal. And none knew the meaning of praise.

Heart-of-the-Earth-and-Sky was much disappointed with the animals and he said to them, "Since you cannot return thanks for your life, you shall not be the ones to rule the earth. Each of you shall stay in the place to which I sent you. There you shall be hunted and your flesh shall become food for the rulers of the world."

Still the time for the first sunrise had not yet come. Only a soft twilight hung over the earth.

Heart-of-the-Earth-and-Sky attempted once more to make creatures fitted to rule his world. Taking clay from the ground, he carefully modeled the pieces into the shapes of men, and he gave them the power to speak.

Yet once more Heart-of-the-Earth-and-Sky was disappointed. The bodies of these clay men were not strong. Neither could they lift up their heads. Although they could speak, they could not think. So when the creator asked them to give him thanks, they could not understand him. Their words were senseless chatter.

So Heart-of-the-Earth-and-Sky caused a heavy rain to fall upon the earth. The earthen bodies turned to mud, and so melting into puddles the first race of men disappeared.

Once more Heart-of-the-Earth-and-Sky attempted to make men. This time he carved pieces of wood in the shapes of men and gave them life and the power to have children.

But these wooden people were no better than the people of clay, for the creator had not given them minds. They could not remember who had made them. Neither could they lift up their heads to speak words of praise to him who had created them.

Heart-of-the-Earth-and-Sky was again disappointed. Again he caused a heavy rain to fall, this time bringing with it a sticky pitch. The wooden men, as they tried to climb the mountains or clamber up the trees, found it hard to move in the sticky slime. What was even worse, the other living things turned against them.

The dogs said, "Why did you not give us our food? The stick was always within reach when you were eating and you drove us away." And the dogs barked and snapped at the wooden men.

The millstones cried out: "When you ground your corn day by day upon our backs, it was squeak, squeak, screech, screech, all the time. Now you shall feel our strength."

The pots and dishes also complained: "You brought us pain and misery continually, burning us over your fires, and smoking our tops and sides. Now we shall make you hot."

Then the wooden men ran hither and thither in terror. When they ran up a mountain, the pots and pans would pull them back. When they climbed the trees the branches hurled them off.

So the second race of men disappeared — the wooden men who had no minds.

Only a few managed to escape into the trees where their children sit to this day, as chattering monkeys.

Still the first sunrise had not yet come. Only a soft twilight hung over the earth.

Again Heart-of-the-Earth-and-Sky attempted to make men. This time he called upon four other gods to help him. These with their secret wisdom said that real men must in some way be made of that greatest of all plants — the corn.

So messengers were sent to the country far to the north to find this wondrous corn — both yellow and white. When at last these messengers returned with the precious corn, the four gods took it and pounded it into meal. The white corn became white meal. The yellow corn became yellow meal.

Then the gods took half the white meal and half the yellow meal and mixed them together with water and moulded the meal into the shape of four men.

The other half of the yellow meal and of the white meal they mixed with water and boiled until it became a thick broth. Then the gods said, "If we feed these men of corn with this rich broth they will grow in strength and muscles. They will even come to have minds and hearts. Then at last we shall have real men who will be able to give praise to their creator."

This time Heart-of-the-Earth-and-Sky was not disappointed. These men were strong and wise. They could think and speak their thoughts. They could even see all over the earth and far beyond. Nothing was hidden from their sight or from their understanding.

Heart-of-the-Earth-and-Sky was pleased with these men with minds. At last he had made men fit to be rulers of the earth.

Then he called the four men to him and said, "Is it not well to be able to think and to speak? Is not the world around you beautiful? What do you think of your life?"

Then these men of corn gave thanks to their creator, saying, "Truly you have given us many things. You have given us power to move with strength and ease. You have given us minds and the power to speak our thoughts. We can see what is near and that which is far off. To you, O Heart-of-the-Earth-and-Sky, we give thanks for all these things."

The destruction of mankind by flood, as pictured by a Mayan artist. The Creator is a serpent in the sky. From its mouth and belly water is pouring down. Two gods of death are helping below.

But the praise from the men with minds did not give the creator the pleasure he had expected.

"It is not well," he thought. "These creatures we have made are almost gods like ourselves. In time they may be able to know and see all things. Then they will be jealous of us and become our rivals. It is not well."

So Heart-of-the-Earth-and-Sky breathed a veil before the eyes of these four men with minds, so that their sight was clouded. They saw as through a misty glass, and only those things that were near at hand. They understood only those things that were simple.

Then Heart-of-the-Earth-and-Sky caused a deep sleep to fall upon the four men. While they slept, he created four beautiful women and put them in the world beside the men. When the men awoke and each one saw a beautiful woman beside him, the knowledge they had lost was for them as though it had never been. And the four men and the four women were happy.

Together they watched the first sunrise dawn upon the earth.

Miwok Indians cracking and grinding acorns and mixing the dough. They are also basket-weaving and have been fishing.

Story from the Miwok Indians of California

The Miwok Indians were once the largest Indian tribe in California. They lived in the valley of the San Joaquin River, their homes extending over this long fertile plain half the length of California and eastward to the Sierra Nevada Mountains.

They lived in cone-shaped huts made of sticks and bark, moving to the mountainsides in the summer and living in the river valley in the winter. Not having learned to plant and raise their own food, they lived mostly on acorns, small animals, and fish. They gathered the acorns in the forests, shelled them, and pounded them into a kind of flour from which they made their bread. They waded out into the river to catch fish by hand or speared them while paddling about on simple wooden rafts. They made their winter clothing out of rabbit fur. They learned to store their acorns away for winter by putting them in baskets woven from willow branches. Then they hung the baskets on tree branches away from animal thieves.

The Miwoks did no reading or writing. When the great chief wished to send a message to his people to ask them to come to a festival, he would send messengers out over the valley with knotted strings to give to the head of each village. He would then hang the knotted string from the branch of a tree and each morning he would untie one of the knots. When all the knots had been untied, everyone knew it was the day to go to the festival.

Even these very primitive people told their wonder stories of the long ago. This one — about how the first animals made man — was their favorite.

The First Animals Make Man

In the far-off beginning of time, when the world was young, there were all kinds of animals living on the earth, but Man had not yet been made.

The Great Spirit, knowing that the Coyote (Kī-ōt) was the smartest of all the animals, gave the work of creating the race of men to him.

As Coyote began to think what kind of creature Man should be, he decided to call the other animals in to help him. So Coyote sent word to all parts of the world, to every kind of animal, saying, "Let one animal of each kind come to a council meeting to plan with me how to create a new creature to be called Man."

As the animals gathered, the mountain lion sat down beside Coyote at his right. The grizzly bear came next, then the deer, the mountain sheep, the beaver, the owl, the mole, and the mouse, and many other animals, the biggest animals being on one side of Coyote and the littlest on the other in a great big circle.

Then Coyote explained why he had called them. "I have called you together to advise me how to create Man. What should he be like? In what ways should he be different from us?"

The mountain lion was the first to speak: "Man should have a strong voice like mine so that he can frighten his enemies by his roar. He should have heavy fur like mine also so that he will always be warm, and he will need strong fangs for catching the smaller animals for food, and he should have a beautiful shaggy tail."

"What a terrible idea that is," said the grizzly bear at once. "With the lion's loud roar Man would frighten away all the other animals. He would have no friends. Of course, Man should be strong but he should not roar. He should be able to stand up on his hind legs as I can do, and he should not have a tail. Tails only catch fleas and dirt."

But the deer objected strongly: "What the bear says is more ridiculous than the proposal made by the mountain lion. Anyone with sense can see that Man should have large branching horns like mine. He will need keen ears and sharp eyes too that can see things far off, and he should be able to run fast. His fur should be light like mine and not heavy like the lion's, so he can be comfortable in the hot weather."

"How foolish you all are!" said the mountain sheep. "Such antlers as the deer has are dangerous. They catch in the bushes and in low-hanging trees. Man should have short curled-up horns like mine so that he will have something hard on the front of his head to butt with. Man cannot live in the world unless he has horns like mine."

"And did you hear the silly thing grizzly bear said about no tail?" screeched the beaver. "I tell you a tail is more important than a leg. How can Man pick up mud and sticks and build a house to live in without a tail?"

At this point Coyote interrupted the discussion. "You are all very stupid," he said. "No one of you can see beyond himself. You might as well take one of your own cubs and

"What should man be like?" asked the Coyote.

call it Man. Man should not be like any one of you. He must be better than any of us. I suppose he will need four legs as we all have, but the bear has a big advantage because he can stand on his hind feet. We must make Man so that he can stand up on two feet, and have two feet left to pick things up with. And I don't think Man should have a tail for it gets in the way. What the deer says about eyes and ears is good, and it would be an advantage not to have heavy fur. Mine is hot in the summer and it gets full of burrs." (Then Coyote thought of fish. No fish could stay out of the water long enough to come to the council meeting.) "The fish has no fur at all," thought Coyote. "It has merely a skin. I will make Man," said Coyote, "without fur and with a soft skin. And I'll make Man very smart like myself."

The Owl had been listening all the while with his eyes closed. But he could not hold back any longer. "All your proposals, and I include Coyote's, are stupid," he cried out. "No one of you has said anything about giving Man wings. How can Man be happy without wings so that he can fly?"

"Wings are not needed," said the mole in a small slow voice. "And what is more, they are dangerous. With wings Man might fly too close to the sun and be burned. Man should be made more like me so that he can burrow in the cool soft earth. Then he will have no need for eyes."

At last the mouse, who had been silent all this time, spoke: "How silly! Man certainly will need eyes to find food. And as for burrowing in the cool soft earth, I can think of nothing more boring."

At this point the council broke up. Every animal was angry and they all began to fight. This quarreling might have gone on for a long time had the animals not noticed Coyote starting to work. One by one they stopped their fighting and set to work also.

Each animal found a lump of clay and began to model from it the kind of creature he had described. They worked busily until the evening, when darkness crept around them. Wearily, first one, and then another, and then another nodded and fell asleep over his work. Finally, all but Coyote were fast asleep.

When the crafty fellow noticed that all the others were asleep, he crept quietly from one model to another and poured water over each one until it was a mass of shapeless mud. Then he went back to finish his own model.

In the morning when the animals wakened and saw what Coyote had done, they were very angry. Some of them started at once to make new models. But long before they had made any real progress in their work, Coyote finished modeling Man and gave him life.

So it came about that Man was made as Coyote had described him in the council of the animals. Man can now stand up straight on two legs. He has no fur on his body and he is smarter than any other animal.

Story from the Wintu Indians
of California

The next story is from another of the Indian tribes that once lived at the northern tip of California. Like the Miwoks, the Wintu were food gatherers rather than planters. They lived in the wide rich valley of the Trinity River not far from the Pacific Ocean and in sight of beautiful snow-capped Mount Shasta.

They lived mostly on acorns, wild potatoes, fish, and clams. The men were skilled at spearing the salmon when they swam up the river in June and July to spawn. When the sweet clover blossoms blooming in abundance all over the valley had faded, the women gathered and pounded the seeds and made cakes of the flour.

As with the Miwoks the coyote was the animal that seemed most like a person. He was always thought of as being especially clever, sometimes helpfully, sometimes harmfully.

The Wintu were a happy people, who delighted in playing in the water and in wading in the shallows to find clams and other shellfish. Shells were collected to use both as ornaments and as money. The people loved to gather for festivals to celebrate special occasions, and to dance and sing. Then the old ones would tell stories of days long gone by and everyone would listen and wonder about Olelbis (Ō-lāl-bis), The-Great-One-Who-Sits-Above-the-Sky, in the beautiful Land of Olelpanti (O-lāl-pän̄t-tee).

Wintu women preparing clover seeds for cooking.

The Road to Olelpanti

In the far-off beginning before there were any Indians living, there was another and very different race of men on the earth. For thousands of years this first race of men had been living together peacefully and happily. But as their numbers multiplied and the earth became crowded, these first people began to quarrel and fight. And Olelbis — The-Great-One-Who-Sits-Above-the-Sky — decided something must be done.

This is what he did. He turned the people one by one into other kinds of living creatures. Some he turned into trees and flowers; others he turned into birds and insects, and still others into land animals and fish. You might say only a handful of people were left. And all of these were old people who would soon die. Among them was Sedit, the Coyote man. The earth in time grew very beautiful with green grassy plains and wooded hills and rivers, where animals of all kinds and birds and fish lived without fear of human hunters.

But Olelbis — The-Great-One-Who-Sits-Above-the-Sky — was lonely without human beings on his world. So he thought out a new plan. He would create a new race of men. He would make the first man and woman come out of the first tree he had made. This time he wanted people to learn to to live together happily and peacefully. How could he help them? Perhaps if he made them immortal they would be happy, he thought. "I will make them so that they will never have to die."

So Olelbis called the two Brothers Hus who lived with him in his beautiful Sky Land of Olelpanti and said to them: "Brothers Hus, I have a great work for you to do. Fly down to the world below where the first tree is growing. Soon I shall cause men and women to come forth out of that tree to live on the earth. But before this happens, you must build a road leading from the earth to Olelpanti. Gather great stones from the hillside and pile them one upon the other like steps leading up to the sky."

"For what purpose do you wish so great a work done, Olelbis?" asked the Brothers Hus.

"It is because I wish that the new race of men, whom I am about to bring forth from the ground, should never have to die. I desire that when they grow old they may be able to renew their youth. I shall, therefore, place two springs at the top of the road that you build, so that when a man grows old, he may climb up this road; and when he reaches the top, he may drink out of one spring and bathe in the other spring. Then his white hair will become dark again and his bent and crippled body will become strong and straight. If an old woman climbs up the road and drinks of the one spring and bathes in the other, she will come out a beautiful young girl. When these people grow old a second time, they may climb the road again and return young and strong to live anew. So shall the men of the earth live on and on forever."

When Olelbis finished speaking, the Brothers Hus said,

"We will do as you have commanded us." So they gathered their tools, and spreading their wings they flew down to the earth to begin the work of building the road of stones.

By the end of the first day, they had piled the stones as high as a house. By the end of the second day, the road was as high as a tall tree. By the end of the third day, it was very high indeed. By the end of the sixth day, the road was touching the clouds. Yet it was still a long way from Olelpanti, and there was much more work to do.

A little before noon on the sixth day, as the Brothers Hus were working, they saw someone walking toward the beginning of the long road. He finally reached the place and sat down beside the road to watch the Brothers as they worked. They knew it was Sedit, the Coyote man, but they said nothing.

"What are you doing here?" Sedit finally asked. "Why are you building this road? It is a great deal of work, and does not seem to be leading anywhere. Can you tell me what it is that you are doing?"

"Olelbis has commanded us to build this road," said one of the Brothers. "Olelbis is planning to make a new race of men come out of the earth. Before he does, he wishes to have a road built reaching from the world to Olelpanti. At the top of the road Olelbis will place two springs."

"That seems strange," objected Sedit, the Coyote man. "There are springs enough on the earth. Why should there be more?"

The other Brother went on with the story. "Olelbis has plans for these springs. As men live on earth they grow old. When men grow old, they become weak and bent and unable

"What are you doing here?" asked the Coyote man.

to do their work. Olelbis does not wish them to grow old and die. So he plans that when men grow old, they can climb this road, and bathe in one spring and drink from the other. Then they will have their youth once more."

Sedit sat quietly for a time, thinking of what the Brothers had said. "Do you believe all this?" he asked at last.

The Brothers Hus were surprised. They had not thought of questioning the plan of Olelbis. But they were interested to know what Sedit meant. So they asked, "Why is it not a good plan?"

"What will people eat if nothing dies?" asked Sedit. "Deer will not die. Fish will not die. Men will not be able to kill anything. What will be left to eat? Nothing but acorns. How uninteresting it will be to live without hunting!"

The Brothers Hus began to be troubled. But Sedit had much more to say.

"I think it is better that men and women should marry and that new children should be born, than that old people should be made young. If they marry, the men will work for the women and the women will work for the men, and so they will help each other. If a man has a wife, he will catch fish and kill deer and bring them home and give them to his wife to cook. And if the woman has a child, her neighbors will say, 'There is a nice baby over there,' and they will go to see it. And so they may be glad together."

"But if someone dies, everyone will mourn and be sad," said the Brothers Hus. "That surely cannot be good."

"When a man grows old, let him die," said Sedit. "When a woman grows old let her die. When they die, the neighbors will come and say, 'A man has died,' or 'A woman has died.'

Then they will make ready to help the relatives of the dead. I think this is better."

"Suppose," continued Sedit, "an old man goes up that road alone and comes back young. He is still alone. Suppose an old woman goes up that road alone and comes back young, she is still alone just as before. They will have nothing to be glad about. They will never make friends. They will never have children. They will never have any fun in the world nor anything to do but to grow old and to go up that road and come back again young. It is not good."

The Brothers Hus had not thought of these things before. Yet the longer they thought, the more true Sedit's words seemed.

"Let us destroy the road that we have built," one Brother finally said to the other. "Let us fly back to tell Olelbis these things. Perhaps he may change his plans for men."

Then Sedit, the Coyote man, turned and walked away, satisfied that he had spoken truly. And the Brothers Hus prepared to fly back to Olelpanti. They pulled several large stones out from the bottom of the pile and the whole road fell, the stones scattering far and wide.

Then just as they were ready to take flight up to Olelpanti, one of the Brothers called back to Sedit.

"Of course, you know that this means that you too will die — just as every other living thing upon the earth will die."

"Come back! Come back!" screamed Sedit. "We must talk some more."

But the two Brothers flew off. Higher and higher they rose, circling above Sedit, until at last he could see them no more.

"What am I to do now? I wish I had not said so much," thought Sedit. "I wish I had not said anything. I do not want to die. What can I do?"

For some time Sedit stood looking around helplessly — till he saw some sunflower plants growing nearby.

"If everything on earth is going to die," said Sedit, "then I am not going to remain on earth. I will make wings for myself, and I will fly to Olelpanti where all living things last forever."

So Sedit picked the leaves off the sunflower plant. He fastened them together in the shape of two wings, and tied the wings to his shoulders. Then he lifted himself as a bird into the air. He flew a short way without any trouble, but the hot noonday sun began to dry the leaves, and one by one they wilted and dropped off. He tried to fly faster in order to reach Olelpanti before the leaves were all gone. But the leaves fell faster than he could fly. Then he felt himself falling. He landed on the pile of rocks which was to have been the road to Olelpanti and was crushed to death.

Olelbis, looking down from Olelpanti, saw all that had happened.

"It is his own fault," he said to the Brothers Hus who had just arrived at Olelpanti. "Sedit is the first of all living things to die. He has been killed by his own words. From this time on, all men will die. They will know the gladness of birth. They will know the sorrow of death. And through these two things together men will come to know love."

A statue of Eros, the God of Love, made in the third century B.C.

Stories from the People of Greece

The ancient Greeks were a very imaginative and thoughtful people. Their gods were almost like supernatural companions whom they both loved and feared. They adorned their temples with sculptured figures of their gods; and they built large open-air theaters where the dramatic stories of their great deeds were acted out year after year. Only two of these stories are given here: "Nyx, the Bird of Night, and Her Golden Egg" and "A Box Full of Troubles." The first tells of the beginnings of the earth and sky; the second, of the beginnings of life and death.

Those who can read the Greek language will find the stories in an ancient book of poems by a Greek poet named Hesiod who lived some 750 years before Jesus. They have been translated into English many times. Most children of the Western world know them almost as well as they know the Bible stories of creation. Eros, Kronos, Epimethus, Prometheus, and Pandora have become names of imaginary personalities often mentioned in books and in conversation.

Nyx, the Bird of Night,
and Her Golden Egg

In the beginning was Nyx, a giant bird with wide-spreading black wings. There was nothing before Nyx. And in the beginning, there was nothing else beside Nyx, except an empty darkness. As a great black cloud, Nyx spread her wide wings over the unbounded darkness.

Then before days began, Nyx, this giant bird of night, laid a golden egg upon the darkness, and in the egg she hid a tiny seed of life. For ages untold, Nyx brooded over her golden egg, as mother birds have brooded ever since over their eggs, till the life within it began to stir. A beautiful god stepped forth — Eros, the god of love — holding a lighted torch.

As Eros came out of the shell, he broke it into two halves. One half, rising, became the sky. The other half turned into the earth. Eros named the sky Uranus (Your'-i-nus). And the earth he called Gaia (Gā'-yä). Now both Uranus and Gaia were alive. They were gods.

Eros, the god of love, led Uranus and Gaia to love each other as men and women love. And after a time, this first divine couple had many children, all of whom were gods who could never die.

Now all of these divine children and grandchildren were

giants and very strong. Some had one hundred arms. Others breathed fire with every breath. One, when he lay down to sleep, stretched over nine acres. These gods could pile one mountain on top of another. They roamed in the whirlwinds and rumbled beneath volcanoes.

But a time came when some of the parents of these gods became afraid of their own giant sons and plotted ways to keep them imprisoned so that they could do no harm.

Kronos (Krō′nös), one of these jealous fathers, decided to swallow his children as soon as each one was born. Mother Rhea, however, after having seen five of her babies disappear in this strange way, worked out a plan for saving her youngest boy, Zeus.

She took a stone shaped like a baby and wrapped it in baby clothes. When Kronos demanded that she give him her baby, Rhea handed him this bundle instead. Kronos without asking any questions swallowed the stone, thinking he had now disposed of his sixth and youngest son.

Then to make sure that Kronos would never see his baby again, Rhea secretly sent Zeus away to a far-off island where she asked some gentle nymphs to take care of him. She sent also several men to live on the island and to keep close watch of her child. Whenever the baby Zeus cried these men were told to beat their drums so that Kronos would not hear the child's crying, or come to kill him.

The years passed quietly by. Zeus grew to manhood. At last Mother Rhea came to the island to see her son for herself. She was pleased with his strength. She knew her Zeus was now more than his father's equal. She said: "My son, you are a child no more. I can no longer protect you from your cruel father. You must now leave this island. You must free us all of his power. Go now to Mount Olympus. Take with you this drug. Find a way to hide it in his drink. When he swallows it, he will have to give up all your five brothers whom he swallowed before you were born."

So Zeus returned with his mother to the mountain home of the gods. He secretly entered the palace. He plotted a way to have the drug put into a glass of wine which his father Kronos would drink when he dined the next time. The plan worked out perfectly. Kronos drank the fatal glass of wine, suspecting nothing wrong. And soon all the five sons he had long ago swallowed were standing in the hall alive and well!

Zeus then entered the hall. He and the five brothers together fought their father. Others of the gods came and joined one side or the other of the battle. The fighting was very fierce. Great rocks were thrown about; lightning flashed, thunder crashed, whirlwinds blew, volcanoes burst into fire. Finally Zeus and those who were with him won in the fight.

The victors chained Kronos and all those who had fought against them, and carried them captive down, down as far below the earth as the sky is above it. They carried them to the land of darkness and night.

Zeus then became the chief ruler of all the gods on Mount Olympus, instead of Kronos. And there was peace. The gods again felt free to wander over the wide earth that lay around and below their heavenly mountain. As they roamed, they made pleasant streams flow through the valleys. They made springs of fresh water burst forth on the mountainsides. They created fruit trees and flowers. Others of the gods hung the stars in the sky and created the sun and the moon, the one to shine by day and the other by night.

At the entrance to their home on the mountain they made a gateway of clouds and set the goddesses of the four seasons to guard the gate. When any of the gods wished to go down to the earth, the clouds were parted. When again the gods wished to return from their wanderings, the goddesses would open the clouds to welcome them back.

> *There on the top of Mount Olympus the gods and the*
> *   goddesses lived.*
> *No storms ever drenched them.*
> *No snow ever clouded the sky.*
> *No cold blasts blew.*
> *The days were always fair with sunshine.*
> *The nights were always peaceful.*
> *There in palaces more beautiful than gold could make*
> *   them, the gods and goddesses lived in perfect happi-*
> *   ness.*

A Box Full of Troubles

As yet in the rest of the world outside Mount Olympus there were no animals or men. Finally Zeus called two of his sons, Prometheus and Epimetheus, to come to his throne. "We need animals and men on the earth," said Zeus. "Go down to the earth and create them. When you have made them, give each some special gift." And Zeus handed his sons a box filled with many good gifts.

So Prometheus and Epimetheus came down from Mount Olympus to the seashore. As they walked together along the sandy clay and gazed out over the ocean, they decided to mold the new creatures from these two things — clay and water. Epimetheus set to work at once to make animals, while Prometheus began to model men. Each went about his work in his usual manner. Epimetheus worked without any plan. Because of this habit of his he had always been called Epimetheus, meaning *after-thought*. He thought about things after he had done them. Prometheus, on the other hand, planned what he would do before starting to model. His name, Prometheus, means *fore-thought;* that is, he was one who thought before he acted.

As the two brothers worked away, each became so absorbed in what he was doing he did not notice what the other one was doing. Epimetheus worked quickly. As soon as he had finished an animal figure he took out something from the box of goodly gifts and gave it to the creature he had made. To the fox Epimetheus gave cunning; to the owl he gave wisdom; the eagle received strength of wing, and the deer, swiftness in running. Epimetheus had finished all the animals before he stopped to see what Prometheus was doing.

Now Prometheus worked slowly and carefully. He was not content with the figure he molded until he had made the very best sort of man he could think of. When finally he had finished his first model, he looked up from his work.

"See, Epimetheus," he cried. "I have finished making the first man. Now I can make more creatures like him and they can go out into the world to live. What gifts are left?"

Epimetheus was startled. Then he was ashamed. He hung his head and whispered, "No gifts are left."

"No gifts for man? It cannot be true! Epimetheus, what have you done?"

"I did not think," said Epimetheus. "While you were working on your one man, I made many animals. As each one was finished, I gave it a gift. Now all the gifts are gone."

"Man must have some special gift," said Prometheus. "Man is to rule over the animals, so he must be made to have more power than they. Somewhere, there must be a gift that is worthy of man. I must find it."

Prometheus walked away down along the shore. As he looked out over the ocean, a great thought came to him. Finally he turned and swiftly walked back to where Epimetheus was still standing.

"I have decided what man must have," he declared. Then he declared defiantly, "It is fire."

Pandora is brought to the earth by Mercury.

"That cannot be," said Epimetheus. "The gods have claimed fire for their own."

"Man must have fire," repeated Prometheus. "I will see that it is secured for this man I have made, and for all his kind."

Prometheus walked away again. This time he knew what he would do. He went straight to the reeds that were growing by the sea. The stalks of the reeds had a hard covering, but inside there was pith, which was soft and damp and would burn slowly. He broke a straight, strong reed from its root and then he returned to Epimetheus.

"With this reed," said Prometheus, "I will go tonight to the door of heaven and steal fire from the sun. In the morning when Phoebus Apollo, the god of the sun, comes forth in his chariot with flaming wheels, I shall stick my reed into the very center of the flames. It will catch fire, and the pith will burn and smolder, while the hard covering of the reed will protect it. In that way, I can bring fire to the earth." Saying no more he left.

Prometheus climbed quickly up to the very door of heaven. Through all the long hours of the dark and silent night he crouched by the door. Finally dawn brightened in the heavens, the door swung open, and then ——

Pandora is presented to Epimetheus.

Phoebus Apollo in his chariot with flaming wheels came forth. He looked neither to the right nor to the left, intent upon the course he was to take. Apollo did not see Prometheus, hidden by the door, but Prometheus saw everything.

Quickly he thrust his reed into the center of the flames, and he held it there until the chariot had passed. Then with his smoldering reed, he quickly went back to earth. The man he had made was standing there beside Epimetheus. Fear darkened the man's face.

"I have it," cried Prometheus.

Gathering some dry leaves in a pile on the ground, he peeled off the hard outer stalk of the reed and placed the smoldering pith under the leaves. He fanned them and he blew upon them. The smoke grew thicker, a spark came forth, a wisp of fire curled up, and then the leaves blazed. Wonder replaced the fear upon the man's face. There was awe in his heart. He had not seen fire on earth before.

As Prometheus molded other men and women, he taught them how to build fires in the doorways of their caves to keep them warm and to frighten away the wild beasts.

Then Prometheus turned and walked away. He knew that Zeus would soon see what he had done and be angry. He had saved men by bringing them fire, but the moment he planned to do it, Prometheus knew he would be punished.

Soon things happened as he had known they must. Zeus, looking down from Olympus, saw men handling fire. Great anger welled up in his heart. "Men were not to have fire," said Zeus. "Fire was to be the property of the gods alone. Men will be too powerful with fire. Prometheus is the only one who could have done this thing. He shall be punished for it."

Zeus then sent Mercury, his faithful messenger, to bring Prometheus before his throne. Prometheus followed Mercury and stood silently before Zeus. "You shall be sentenced to lie chained forever to a rock on the peak of a high mountain while vultures from time to time will fly at you and eat your flesh," declared Zeus.

Prometheus looked straight before him. He did not turn his head, but followed his captors as they led him forth. In his heart he knew he had done a good thing. He was ready to take his punishment. Men now had fire and that was enough.

But Zeus was not satisfied to punish only the one who had stolen fire. He called a council of gods.

"Men have the fire which Prometheus has stolen. Men, too, must share the punishment," said Zeus from his throne high on Olympus. "Mercury, bring Vulcan before me." So Mercury brought Vulcan from his forge and led him to Zeus. Vulcan stood silently before the throne waiting to receive his order.

"Vulcan," Zeus decreed, "go and fashion a maiden who will have the form of a goddess, and bring her here that each of us may give her some beauty or some charm to attract the men Prometheus has made. When you mix the clay, mix in guile and cunning, a shameless mind and a deceitful nature. Go!"

When Vulcan had finished his task he came once more before the throne, leading a maiden by the hand. She was very beautiful and the gods and goddesses were pleased with her. Each one gave her a gift. Athene arrayed her in clothes of gleaming beauty. The Hours twined flowers in her hair. Mercury gave her flattering words to say to men, and the

Pandora and Epimetheus when the jar is opened. Hope
waits inside the jar, holding a flower.

Graces put necklaces and precious jewels upon her. Even
Zeus gave her a gift. His was curiosity. And he named the
maiden Pandora, meaning "Gifted of the Gods."

Then Zeus prepared a box and filled it with all kinds of
evil things — pain, fear, envy, pride, deceit, hate, sickness, and
death. Turning again to Mercury, Zeus said, "Take Pandora
down to the earth and give her to Epimetheus. As you leave
her to return to Olympus, give her this box and tell her it is a
good gift only if she never opens it. The day she looks inside
the box, evil will come to her and to all men."

Long weeks and months went by and Epimetheus and
Pandora were happy together. They visited the homes of men,
they walked through the fields and knew many joys. But
again and again, Pandora became very curious about the box.
"The gods and goddesses gave me many beautiful things.
The things in the box may be lovelier still."

Finally one day when Epimetheus was not at home,
Pandora could no longer control her curiosity. "I simply must
see what is in the box," she thought. "I will just lift the lid a

little bit and peep inside." But the moment the cover was loosened, all the evil creatures imprisoned inside came forth. Pandora ran away screaming, not knowing which way to turn.

Epimetheus was not far away and came running home. When he saw what had happened, he fastened the lid down again. But it was too late. Pain and hate, jealousy and fear, deceit and envy, sickness and death — all had come forth. Now that they were free, they rushed into every corner of the world.

Late that night, Epimetheus and Pandora heard a faint noise coming from the closed box. A voice seemed to cry, "I am Hope. Let me out." For a long time they would not go near the box. But Epimetheus finally said, "It cannot be worse than the things that were freed. Perhaps it really is Hope as it claims to be."

So they opened the box again, and Hope came out. She went forth into the world and put courage into the hearts of men.

So it was when the world was young that Prometheus gave men the wondrous gift of fire. So it was that all mankind were punished by the coming of evil things — pain, fear, envy, pride, deceit, hate, sickness, and death. And so it has been that men have never lost the hope of conquering all these evils.

Zuni prayer plumes.

Story from the Zuni Indians of New Mexico

Today a Zuni pueblo or village nestles at the foot of the tall red cliffs of Thunder Mountain in northern New Mexico. Before the Europeans came to America, there were many more Zuni Indians than now.

Theirs were the oldest skyscrapers in America. Halfway up the side of some steep cliff back on a wide ledge, they would cut rooms out of the solid rock. Above these rooms and set back still further into the mountainside, they would cut out

An Indian pueblo today, near Taos, New Mexico.

another row of rooms, and above this still another level —
four or five stories of rooms they would cut out, until they had
made a tall many-roomed stone castle, hiding far up against
and within the side of the steep cliff. When someone wished
to pass from one level to the next, a ladder would be set up
against the wall for a stairway.

On some ledge, wider than the rest, these Zuni folk
would gather to hear the teller of stories repeat his tales. Sitting in the cool of the day, they would watch the setting sun
paint pictures of glory upon the clouds and shed its rainbow
glow over the tops of the mountains. At such a time they
would feel a great goodness shining in the Sun-Father's face
and they would be content.

"Out of the Caves of the World" was the greatest of all

their stories as well as the longest. As the old Indian storytellers gave it, the story took four hours in its telling. When
the storyteller once began, however, he was not allowed to
stop until he had finished, for the people felt somehow that it
was wrong to leave the story only half told. All the Zuni folk
looked forward to the one great day in the year when this,
the noblest of all their stories, would be told.

In an Indian wigwam a Zuni priest draws a prayer picture
in the sand.

Out of the Caves of the World

In the far-off beginning, there was no earth or sky. Only a watery waste with the Sun-Father above. There were no animals; and no people. For ages uncounted the Sun-Father shone on this watery waste until, because of the warmth of his great light, a green scum began to grow on the top of the great waters. Slowly the scum spread. It grew wider and wider and thicker and thicker until at last it became the Four-Fold-Containing-Earth-Mother.

Earth-Mother was called the Four-Fold-Containing-Earth-Mother because there were four folds or levels within the earth. Three of these were dark caves under the earth; the fourth was the land that we know today.

The deepest level was a dark, damp cave called the Cave of the Sooty Depth. Here were the seeds of men. In the darkness and the dampness of this cave the seeds grew and expanded until finally they burst their husks, even as hatching birds burst their eggshells or moths come forth from cocoons.

For a time the creatures who came out of the seeds grew in this Cave of the Sooty Depth. They were unfinished beings, slimy and cold and covered with scales. They crawled like reptiles through the cave and over one another, not caring where they went or what they did. Time passed and these unfinished creatures grew and increased so that the cave became full to overflowing.

Then the Beloved Twain led all the man-creatures whom they could persuade up the vine-ladder. . . .

Again the Sun-Father, high above the waters, sent forth his life-giving light. This time he shone upon foam that was floating upon the water, till by the power of his light two gods arose from the foam who were called the Beloved Twain.

When the Beloved Twain had arisen from the foam, the Sun-Father commanded them, "Go down to the lowest cave and lead the man-creatures up through the other caves until they reach the upper air. Guide them and help them along the way."

Deep into the earth went the Beloved Twain. Finally they came to the deepest cave of all, the Cave of the Sooty Depth. Here the man-creatures were crawling about. The Beloved Twain saw vines, too, growing in the darkness. One of the Beloved Twain breathed upon the vines and they began to grow taller and taller. While this was happening, the other god wove the branches of the vines together so that they formed a ladder. When the ladder of vines was finished it reached to the next cave above.

Then the Beloved Twain led all the man-creatures whom they could persuade up the vine-ladder into the next cave of the earth. Some would not follow but remained in the lowest cave.

In the second cave the sooty dark gave way to a darkness like that of a stormy night. The cave was small, but it was larger and higher than the deepest cave. Here, too, the man-creatures grew and multiplied. Some of them lost their scales. Some of them learned to raise themselves on their hind feet. Slowly the man-creatures were becoming more man-like.

Time passed. The second cave, like the Cave of the Sooty Depth, became full to overflowing. Once more the Beloved

Twain breathed upon the vines and a new ladder grew. The Beloved Twain led the man-creatures to another level of the Four-Fold-Containing-Earth-Mother. Again some of the creatures remained behind, never to change and grow as did those who followed the Beloved Twain.

Before the man-creatures were led up this ladder, however, the Beloved Twain spoke to them. "You are about to go into another cave world. There you will grow to be different from one another. Some of you are to become red men and some white. Others will become tawny, and some yellow."

Then the Beloved Twain divided the man-creatures into groups. Each group was led separately up the vine-ladder. First, those who were to become red, then those who were to be white. Next those who were to be tawny, and then the yellow.

In this way the man-creatures came into the third level, or cave, of the Four-Fold-Containing-Earth-Mother. Here the darkness was like that of a valley lit by starlight, and the cave was higher and wider than the others. In this cave each of the groups lived apart from the others. Here they grew, and changed, and multiplied, until at last this cave, too, was filled to overflowing as the others had been. Then once more the Beloved Twain led upward those who would follow. Again some remained behind, and because they did so, they have not changed through all the ages.

In this way man-creatures were finally led into the fourth level of the Four-Fold-Containing-Earth-Mother, the world of the upper air which we know. Here the brightness was too great for them, even though the light was only that of the

Evening Star and the Moon. When morning came and the Sun-Father himself appeared in the east, the man-creatures were blinded by his brightness and fell down on their faces before him.

These first men lived for a time right there beside the cave from which they had come, till the Beloved Twain called them together. "You are not to remain as you are now," they said. "The time will come when you will no longer crouch low, but stand proudly upright. Your fingers and toes that are now webbed will become separated so that you can use them for things you have not yet dreamed of. You will lose your tails, and there will be no scales or heavy hair on your bodies. You will become warm. The earth will change too. Now it is cold and wet, but it will not always be so. There are earthquakes rumbling about you now, but you will not always hear them."

"You must listen carefully," said the Beloved Twain. "You have a long journey to make to a place called the Middle Land. It will take you many years to reach it, and by the time you are there you will be very different from what you are now. As long as you hear the rumble of the earthquakes, travel on to the east toward the Sun-Father. If ever the earthquakes stop, then you shall stop also. Remain in that place until the earthquakes sound once more. They will be your signal to travel on. When finally you reach the Middle Land the earthquakes will stop forever."

So these first men started their long journey to the Middle Land. Here, too, a few remained behind, and never changed. They never learned to stand up straight. They kept their scales and webbed toes and fingers and long tails.

One day an earthquake came, more terrible than any they had heard before. It was so loud and awful that these first men dared not move until it was over. Mountains rose, canyons sank, and in the confusion rocks were scattered over the earth. Many of the huge wild animals that had bothered the first men were never seen again. At last there was stillness.

In the silence these first men realized that this was their first resting place. So here they stayed and made shelters for themselves and lived in peace until once more they heard the rumblings of another earthquake. Then at a word from the Beloved Twain, they struggled on, but some, too tired to walk farther, remained behind and lost their chance to change.

Time after time the same things happened: a journey, the ceasing of the earthquakes, the resting in peace, then the coming of another earthquake as a signal that they must move on. Each time a few remained behind and so ceased their changing, but most of these first men struggled on, and with each lap of the journey they became more like the men of today.

In one resting place they lost their tails and their webbed feet, and hands became separated into fingers. In each resting place they found the earth becoming more like the earth we know today. The slime and mud turned to soft earth. This earth became covered with grass. Then flowers and bushes and trees grew up. In one resting place the first men found corn, and learned to plant and harvest it. At last, they were able to walk upright. They could look straight before them as they went, and they could turn their heads to see the beauty all about them. They had grown in power, in courage, in beauty, and in wisdom.

So on and on the Beloved Twain led these first men. At
last they reached the Middle Land. What is more, they became men, strong and straight and true. There in the Middle
Land they built their houses, and there they still live. Above
them the Sun-Father still shines with the power of his light.

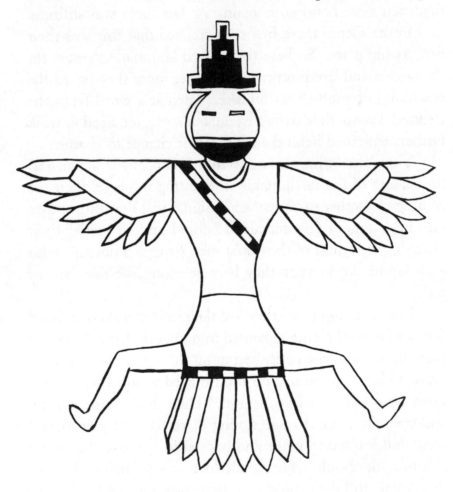

Stories from the Scientists
of the World

No movie theater can present a picture half so marvelous as the one that is shown every clear night free to all people everywhere in the world. This is the wondrous picture of thousands of bright stars moving slowly, in one grand formation, across the dark dome of the sky. From the time when human beings were first able to stand up straight and lift their eyes to the skies, this nightly starlit sky has been arousing curiosities and stirring men's minds to wonder. What are these lights? How far away are they? What makes them move? How many of them are there? Is our earth the biggest of worlds? Are there people living on other worlds?

But the stars circle the earth in silence. They answer no questions. Men have had to figure out answers for themselves.

Night after night, year after year, patiently they have watched and timed the moments when the stars appeared and disappeared, and made maps of their paths in the sky. The more men learned, the more curious they became, and the more carefully they watched. Even during the last twenty-five years, modern astronomers have discovered so many new things about the earth, the sun, and the stars that they have almost completely changed their theories about how everything might have begun in the first place.

Past Discoveries Help Scientists Today

This very rapid progress in recent years has not come about, however, because men today are so much smarter than the men who lived before. It is due to the fact that the scientist today is able to start where the men of the past left off. He can build on foundations laid by thousands of patient explorers and watchers of the sky who have gone before.

The scientist of today has not only the advantage of starting with what men before had already found out; he has also the advantage of having the use of hundreds of invented instruments that can multiply for him many times what human eyes alone can see or human ears alone can hear. Perhaps the two most important of these instruments are the microscope and the telescope. And both of these can be called recent inventions. When Columbus set sail across the Atlantic to prove that the earth was round, he had neither a microscope nor a telescope. In fact it was not until one hundred years after Columbus that Galileo first pointed a little telescope at the moon. And it was not even that long ago when Anthony Leeuwenhoeck first used a microscope to look at a drop of water and discovered tiny living creatures which no man before him ever dreamed existed.

The first microscopes and telescopes seem to us now like toys compared with the wonderful instruments of today. Leeuwenhoeck's microscope could enlarge an object three or four times, but today's electronic microscopes can make objects look 100,000 times larger than they really are. Galileo's little telescope could show the moons rolling around the planet Saturn, but men using the great telescopes of today can take photographs of millions of stars and clusters of stars that are completely invisible to the most far-seeing eyes of stargazers. With these wonderful instruments modern scientists have discovered surprising new things about the universe which even the best-educated men of fifty years ago could not have imagined.

Three Ways in Which the Thinking of Scientists Has Changed

These new discoveries have led the scientists to change their thinking about the universe in three especially important ways. (1) They have found that the universe is very much older than they once imagined. (2) They have found also that the universe is very much larger than they used to think. (3) They have found that the tiniest things hold the secret to the understanding of the largest things. Let us examine these three large ideas as now believed by the scientists.

The Universe Is Much Older Than Men Used to Imagine

In the old English Bible, which we call the King James translation made in the year 1611, the translators put the date of the creation of "the heaven and the earth" in the margin alongside the first verse of the first chapter of Genesis. This date was 4004 B.C., only about six thousand years ago. Even the best-educated man of that time in England thought the date was correct. In contrast, geologists today say that the earth must be about four billion years old or older.

How Do Scientists Figure Out the Earth's Age?

A geologist today knows all the kinds of rocks on the earth by name. Give him a rock to examine and he will tell you its history, how it was formed, what it was made out of, how the different elements in it could have combined to make the rock. What is even more remarkable, he will be able to figure out (if you give him time enough) how long it took the rock to change from being a gas to being a liquid, and then to cool and to harden into the rock it now is. For everyone is now agreed that in the beginning the earth was one huge cloud of white-hot gas.

When a geologist today sees layers of rocks showing on the edge of a cliff or on a mountainside, he thinks of these layers as being the pages of the great book of the earth laid open for men to read. The story of the beginnings of the earth's history is on the pages deepest down. Rock pages are hard to turn, and Nature does not write in any of man's languages, yet the geologist has learned to read this book of the earth. In between the rock pages Nature has captured and preserved as fossils the skeletons of some of the living creatures that wandered over the rocks. The scientists have collected these fossils and studied and compared them until now they can make charts showing the order in which the different animals and plants lived, and what they were like.

Scientists in their laboratories have been studying also samples of sea water to find out how much salt is in it: They think that in the beginning all the earth's oceans were filled with fresh water and that salt has been slowly collecting in them. The waves breaking against the shores have broken up the rocks, pounding them into sand. Slowly the salt that was in them has been washed into the oceans. It is known that the sea water is saltier now than it was fifty years ago, or even twenty years ago. By comparing the records of the ocean's saltiness year by year, the scientists have figured out how long it has taken the oceans to become as salty as they are now. Their answer to this long arithmetic problem is that the world was covered with one great ocean of fresh water probably nearly four billion years ago.

The Universe Is Much Larger Than Men Once Supposed

When men could not travel except by foot or on a donkey's back, when there were no telescopes to enlarge man's view of the universe, it was entirely reasonable to suppose that the earth was flat, resting perhaps on the back of a giant turtle or floating quietly on a boundless sea. As long as men were dependent on their own two eyes when they looked at the sun, moon, and stars, it was natural to assume that these lights were moving around the earth, fastened to a great dark dome.

But now everyone accepts the idea that the earth is no longer the center of everything, that it is a large ball, spinning completely around like a top every twenty-four hours and also rolling through space around the sun at the speed of over 70,000 miles an hour. But the earth simply does not seem to us to be spinning like a top; neither does it seem to be whirling through space at a terrific speed. It travels without a sound or a jar. No matter on what part of the earth one walks, he always feels he is standing right side up and on the top; yet on a spinning ball half the people at any one time must be walking upside down on the bottom. This strange situation is explained to us by saying that the earth acts like a magnet. It has a power called *gravity* that holds us tight and keeps us always feeling right side up.

Although such a picture of the earth contradicts what our eyes see and what our feelings tell us, we accept this picture of the earth as true because we know that the scientists have tested and proved these ideas over and over again. Only the very small child and the great philosophers seem any longer to be amazed, and ask what is this mysterious power called *gravity*?

The scientist is like a person starting out to put a jigsaw puzzle together. At first he makes some wild guesses about one of the small pieces. He thinks he knows what it is a part of. Then slowly as he is able to fit a few pieces together, he finds the picture becoming very different from what he had expected. So it has been with the astronomers. As better and bigger telescopes have been made, they have been able to get larger and larger views of the things in space, and the ideas they began with have been changing.

From the view the scientists now have of the universe, they see the earth as one in a number of spinning balls, rolling through space around the sun. And what is even more amazing is that, as far as they can now tell, everything, everywhere, is always moving. Nothing anywhere is standing still. And everywhere there is this strange mysterious attraction that one thing has for another — called *gravity* — that keeps drawing things together, neither too tightly nor too loosely, yet somehow always holding all things.

Our Solar System

Which are the earth's closest neighbors in the skies? Surrounding the earth ball on all sides is a deep ocean of air, probably five hundred miles deep. We work and play at the bottom of this deep ocean. As yet our best planes can take us up into it only about ten or twenty miles. Rockets without human pilots are being shot up through this atmosphere higher and higher each year. We are promised man-made satellites soon that will reach even greater heights and that can carry human passengers.

What is beyond this atmosphere? Men are growing more and more curious to know. How cold is it? How hot? How dangerous are the cosmic rays from the sun? The meteors? How would it feel to be where the earth's gravity no longer pulls? Could man survive? Once up, could he return alive? All these and many more questions scientists are asking. They are hoping some day to reach the moon even though it is not a mere one thousand miles away but 250,000 miles away!

Beyond the moon is the giant sun — 93,000,000 miles beyond. Although our earth is rolling round the sun at a speed of over 70,000 miles an hour, it takes the earth an entire year to make the rounds. Closer to the sun than our earth are Mercury and Venus, and farther out, whirling round in larger and larger orbits, are six other planets. If we imagine the sun as being the size of a basketball, our earth would be about the size of a pea whirling around it a distance of fifty-four feet away, while Pluto, the farthest away of all the planets, would be circling in an orbit half a mile still farther away. We could not even see our earth if we were living on Pluto. This tremendous whirling disk of planets and moons swinging round and round the sun we call our *solar system*.

A Galaxy Surrounds Our Solar System

This tremendous solar system of ours is but one among millions of other solar systems. It is hard to realize when one looks up at a sky full of stars that every star we can see (except the planets, which are not really stars) is actually a sun, each sun the center of its own solar system of planets and moons. And all these solar systems, including our own, are swinging as separate whirling disks round and round a larger center of gaseous clouds. This very much vaster whirlpool, made up of a hundred thousand million solar systems, we call our *galaxy*. On a clear night we can see the edge of our galaxy stretching as a misty strip of white across the sky. We call it the Milky Way. Our little solar system is whirling somewhere near the edge of this giant galaxy.

The size of this our galaxy can be put down on paper, but no human mind can picture the meaning of the figures. The astronomers no longer use ordinary miles in counting the distance from one edge of this galaxy to the other. Instead they speak of "light-years." A "light-year" is the distance sunlight can travel through space during one year's time. This is made the measuring stick because sunlight travels faster than anything else. It travels 186,000 miles a second! Multiply that

A nebula far beyond our galaxy, seen edge on. It is named Corna Berenices.

number by the number of seconds in one year, and you will know how many miles a "light-year" means. Measured by this giant scale, the light from the sun takes eight minutes to reach the earth. Yet for light to reach us from the nearest star, belonging to another solar system, it takes eight years. And for light to travel from one rim of our galaxy to the opposite rim it takes sixty thousand years! What a galaxy to be living in!

Other Galaxies Surround Our Galaxy

But we cannot stop here even in our own giant galaxy. Now that the astronomers have the wonderful telescope on Mount Palomar in California, they tell us they can see out into space far beyond our own galaxy. They are reporting millions more galaxies. Some look like whirlpools with arms of fiery gaseous stars stretching out in all directions. Others are loose clusters of fiery mist, and still others appear as round balls of fire. Actually each is a cluster of millions of stars. Some of these galaxies are larger than our own. Others are smaller. Some, the astronomers think, are just beginning to form into galaxies, while others are older. Dr. Harlow Shapley says that the light from the galaxies farthest away probably began traveling our way two thousand million years ago!

Such numbers bewilder us. We cannot imagine them. The size of the universe is beyond man's measuring.

The Smallest Things Hold the Secret to the Largest Things

Our imaginations grow weary as we try to imagine such tremendous distances. Millions of galaxies and billions of suns whirling in outer space, millions of light-years away! So let

A nebula seen from above. It is named Ursa Major.

us change the subject for a while, and think about the very small things.

The smallest things have always made men curious. For centuries scientists have been trying to take things apart, hoping to find the smallest parts out of which they were made. Over two thousand years ago Democritus, a Greek philosopher, said he believed there was this smallest part to every kind of thing in the whole universe. This smallest part he called an *atom,* meaning in Greek something that cannot be taken apart. Democritus thought that the differences between things might be because these atoms had different shapes or because they were combined or put together in different ways.

This was a clever guess and like many thoughtful guesses it has been proved to be partly true. Our own period of history will probably long be known as the *Atomic Age* because our scientists were the first to learn how to break certain atoms apart and to find out what they are like inside. This great discovery has not only changed man's thinking about atoms. It has changed man's thinking about everything in the whole universe and about its beginnings.

What Then Are Atoms Like Inside?

Atoms are so small that no microscope has yet been invented that can show a clear picture of the inside of an atom. By using a camera to enlarge the picture seen through a microscope, photographs of atoms have been made. Yet even though these two instruments together have magnified the atom 175,-000,000 times, still the atoms show up simply as shadowy clouds, with no hint of what the inside of an atom is like.

Scientists have found other ways of finding out about

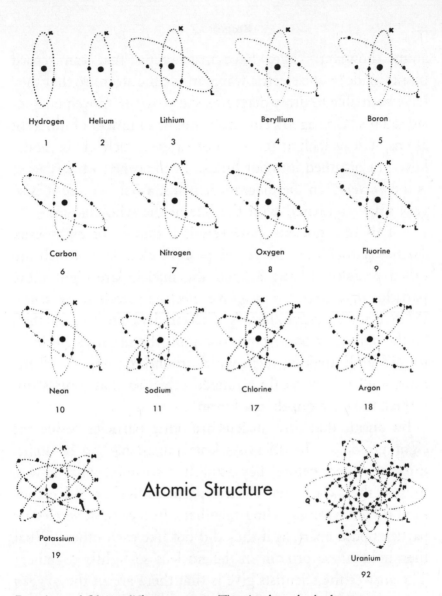

Hydrogen
1

Helium
2

Lithium
3

Beryllium
4

Boron
5

Carbon
6

Nitrogen
7

Oxygen
8

Fluorine
9

Neon
10

Sodium
11

Chlorine
17

Argon
18

Potassium
19

Atomic Structure

Uranium
92

Drawings of fifteen different atoms. The simplest, the hydrogen atom, is first; and the most complicated, the uranium atom, is last.

atoms, however. They have instruments that can record marks made by the electric waves inside the atoms so that they have been able to draw diagrams showing the movements inside atoms. On page 153 are diagrams of a number of different atoms. Let us look at the atom of *oxygen,* such as you and I have just breathed into our lungs. In the center of this atom is the *nucleus.* In the diagram it is just a dot because it is so very small compared with the size of the whole atom.

This tiny nucleus, however, is a bundle of eight even smaller particles or charges of positive electricity which are called *protons.* Flying around the nucleus are eight more particles or charges of negative electricity, called *electrons.* Positive and negative charges of electricity attract each other. So the bundle of positive protons pulls the negative electrons toward itself, making them whirl around the nucleus all the time, and in very neatly arranged orbits so that, unless disturbed, the electrons do not bump.

But inside that tiny nucleus are other particles beside the eight protons. The scientists knew there had to be something else there before they actually discovered what it was, because they knew that electric particles that are all of one kind do not naturally cling together. In fact positive electric particles push apart, as if they did not like each other. What then holds these protons in the nucleus so tightly together? The answer the scientists give is that there are in the *oxygen nucleus* eight more particles called *neutrons.* This means they are neither positive nor negative electric charges; they are neutral. They belong to neither side and can act as peacemakers, we might almost say, between the eight protons so that they stick together while the eight electrons go darting swiftly round and round them. It has amazed and puzzled the scientists to find how tightly these protons are held together by the neutrons. Until they found a way to pull this nucleus apart, they could not break the atom apart.

Atoms, Atoms, Everywhere

Scientists now believe that all things everywhere in the whole universe are made up of atoms — atoms in the sun, the moon, the stars; atoms in tigers and lions, in trees and stones, in the air we breathe, in the water we drink, in the ground we walk on. We ourselves — our bodies — are made of billions of atoms. And the bodies of all plants and fish and birds and animals are also made of atoms.

How Many Kinds of Atoms Are There?

Anyone who had not already been shown the answer to this question would naturally expect to find that there were a very great many different kinds of atoms — the universe being so gigantic and so full of things. But surprising as it is, this is not at all the case. Actually there are thought to be only about a hundred different kinds of atoms in all the whole universe. A very small number for everything everywhere! What is even more amazing is that these one hundred different kinds of atoms have all the same general kind of pattern. There is always a nucleus and there are always one or more particles of negative electricity flying around this nucleus. And these one hundred or so kinds of atoms can be arranged in a neat row, beginning with the simplest kind at one end and ending with the most complicated kind at the other end. An atom of *hydrogen* is the simplest of all atoms since it has but one proton in its nucleus and one electron flying around it. Next comes the atom of *helium,* which has two protons in its nucleus and two electrons flying around it. The next kind of atom has three protons in its nucleus, the next four, the next five, and so on. Oxygen, as we have seen, has eight protons, and *uranium* has ninety-two protons in its nucleus. And in all of these one hundred kinds of atoms there are exactly as many electrons as there are protons, and in every nucleus there are as many neutrons in addition as are needed to hold the nucleus bundle together.

If we could become microscopic pygmies and walk around among the atoms, what a lot of questions we would want to ask! It is not strange that the scientists, when they had learned these things about atoms, determined to find out more. They felt that if they could once fathom the mystery within a single atom they would have a key that would open door after door into an understanding of the mystery in all things.

Hundreds of years ago, philosophers began saying that the world of very small things and the world of the very large things were somehow connected. But not until the scientists began drawing diagrams of atoms did anyone guess that the small and the large could be so much alike. Who looking at the diagram of an oxygen atom can fail to see how much it is like a diagram of our solar system? The nucleus seems like a microscopic sun, and the electrons whirling around it seem like planets. When we try to imagine systems even larger than our own, we see that the microscopic atom is also like a galaxy with a gaseous center of star dust, around which thousands of solar systems revolve. Everywhere on the earth and throughout all space the general pattern is the same. Particles — microscopic and gigantic — circling around their centers. Circles within circles, circles beside circles, circles around circles. Everything is moving. Nothing is still. Each part attracting another part or pulling away, always swinging, always dancing round and round — as if alive. Whether we are looking at stars and planets or thinking of electrons and protons and neutrons that we cannot see, it is always the same.

These then are some of the important discoveries scientists have made in recent years which have led them to change their theories about how everything may have begun. They have found that there are only a few patterns by which all patterns are made. There are a few simple patterns from which the complex patterns grow. The tiniest atoms are like the greatest galaxies. This very old and very gigantic universe, it now seems, is understandable. The scientist knows he can depend on it and work with it as he finds out its plans or its laws — that is, as he finds out how it works and understands the parts out of which it is made.

So the scientists with their microscopes and the astronomers with their telescopes have been working together. What one group has learned about the smallest things has been throwing light on what the other group has needed to know about the biggest things. The new discoveries that scientists have been making about things near at hand have been throwing light on things the astronomers have wanted to know about things millions of miles away in space.

How Then Do Living Things Begin Today?

This is the kind of question the scientists began with.

How do plants begin now? Or animals or people? Do they appear suddenly full grown? Or are they first small? *Every single living thing, so far as we know, begins as a tiny speck — as a single cell.* It is the same with the biggest whale as it is with the smallest insect or piece of moss. It has been the same for every person who has ever lived in all the world, whether he became a giant or a pigmy. Everything alive starts as a microscopic single cell. Probably the very first life millions of years ago began the same way. This is how our scientists reasoned.

Has the same kind of beginning been true of things that are not alive? Did minerals and stones begin with their simplest and smallest parts? Did they begin as single atoms? and were the first atoms the simplest of all the atoms? Did the hydrogen atom come first while the universe was in the making? And then did helium, with two protons and two electrons in it, come next? And was the helium atom made before there was the next atom in the line? Were all these primary elements or things in the universe made one after another in some kind of order? This seemed a likely guess.

How then could the simplest atoms have been made? And how did the simpler atoms change into the next more complicated ones? Until a few years ago no one had ever found out how to make one kind of atom change into another kind. No one had found out how to change even a hydrogen atom into an atom of helium. But when the hydrogen bomb exploded, that is exactly what the scientists had succeeded in doing. They actually saw for themselves what happened when hydrogen became helium. Never before had men seen such a terrific explosion. The energy released lifted the temperature around until it was equal to that of the sun.

It would be appropriate some time to talk of the cruel horror of using the hydrogen bomb to destroy people. Here we are thinking only of the change that this experience brought about in the scientists' thinking on how everything might have begun. For many years it had been known that the sun was not burning as an ordinary fire burns. If it had been such a burning, the sun would long ago have been turned into ashes. The scientists had also long thought that the sun's terrific heat was probably produced by continuous atomic explosions of some kind. But not until they themselves had actually exploded the hydrogen bomb could they understand how such explosions could be made. When they saw hydrogen actually changing into helium and found out what happened, they became convinced that they had done on a very small scale what was taking place continually on a very large scale in all the suns in space. In fact, they came to believe they had done on a very small scale what might have happened near the very beginning of time, when the whole universe was nothing but hydrogen gas.

So out of study and experimenting with the smallest things, the scientists of today have been unlocking doors into greater and greater understanding of the happenings in the universe as a whole. At the present time there seem to be two slightly different theories among scientists regarding beginnings. We will present them briefly so that we may compare them, ask more questions, and share with the scientists some of their feelings of wonder and awe.

Beginnings of Earth, Sun, and Stars

In the beginning was *energy*. All the energy the universe needed to start becoming. In the beginning this energy was without any patterns or forms. Nothing was separated from anything else. There were as yet no atoms separated from other atoms. There were not even protons, or electrons, or neutrons. The energy was chaotic — without order.

In the beginning this formless energy would have been invisible to human eyes had there been any eyes there to watch. Yet this formless and invisible energy was very restless — more restless than the burning flames of a million furnaces, more restless than the electricity in a million dynamos. We might say the energy was darting about, circling, pushing, pulling, and shooting out at random, moving at the speed of light.

Then came the momentous moment! A gigantic chaotic explosion! A brilliant blaze, as bright as the light from all the stars in the universe combined, lighted up space. It must have been as if a million H-Bombs had exploded at once. Clouds of hydrogen and helium and other gases were shot out with such violence that sparks and pieces of these first grains of hot dust were blown in all directions throughout space — eventually to millions of light-years away.

With this great explosion the invisible energy became visible. The formless began to take on forms and patterns of movement. Protons and electrons and neutrons appeared.

The protons began pairing with the electrons. Single electrons circling round single protons. So the first atoms of hydrogen were formed, for that wondrous invisible force, called *gravity,* now began drawing particles of matter toward one another.

Gravity also began drawing the great clouds of hot gases rushing out into space back toward the center, and they began rolling round it in great orbits and circles. These massive clouds began to separate into lesser clouds; and within these lesser clouds the pieces of hot dust began to gather in swirling spirals and round clusters and finally into balls. The smaller balls began spinning around the larger ones. The larger balls later became the suns that kept the smaller balls revolving around them. The smaller balls cooled faster than the larger balls and have become the planets and satellites in the sky.

In some such way as this it is thought that all the millions of galaxies in space were started whirling in their great orbits. And within the galaxies, the smaller solar systems began whirling in their smaller orbits. Spinning disks and balls of gaseous clouds, stars and worlds. Each ball spinning on its own axis and whirling round a larger spinning ball. In circles within circles, with the whole family of galaxies whirling around the greater center from which all came in the beginning.

The first great explosion occurred, it is thought, about six billion years ago. It probably took our small earth two or more billion years after that to become cool enough so that its gases began changing into molten material, then began hardening into stones, and some of the stones could crumble into pebbles and sand. Hot mists spurted out of the earth's white-hot center and spread above and around the earth. The mists, cooling, finally fell as rain and formed rivers, lakes, and oceans. The outside of the earth ball cooled faster than the inside. A crust formed that wrinkled like the drying skin of an apple. The mountains and valleys were formed and slowly the earth took on the shape it has today.

The story, however, is far from its end. New suns and new worlds are still being formed. Galaxies are still gathering their whirling clouds of hot dust particles into balls. Some of these balls are cooling into planets, and new solar systems are coming into being.

On the other hand, other star clusters seem to be growing old. They are losing their heat. The power that holds them together seems to be weakening. They seem about ready to fall apart.

What is more, the astronomers think they see signs that the distant galaxies are flying apart. The space between them seems to be growing wider and wider. The universe seems to be expanding like a balloon. This is very puzzling. What can it be that is happening?

Some of the astronomers think that this means the universe isn't as filled with energy as it once was. The amount of energy given it in the beginning is being used up. The stars are cooling. If this expanding and cooling continues, the whole universe will at last become cold. The galaxies will fall apart, and worlds will crumble. No life will be able to survive. If this should come about, the astronomers assure us that it cannot happen for at least six billion more years.

Another group of astronomers have a different idea about

what this expanding means. They say something like this: Why think of the universe as something dead, like a machine or a balloon, that has in it just so much energy and when the energy is used up the machine must stop? Instead, why not think of the universe as an enormous *living body* that is growing as all living bodies naturally grow? If the Universe is living, then as it gets larger and larger it is not growing emptier and emptier. Instead, this *living body,* the *universe,* is continually adding new parts to its body. It is growing rather than merely spreading itself. As living bodies continually create new cells to take the places of the old cells that wear out, so the universe may be continually creating new atoms of hydrogen to replace the ones that lose their energy.

Dr. Fredrick Hoyle, a noted astronomer of England, thinks he has figured out just about how many new atoms of hydrogen the universe needs to make every year in order for it to be growing as fast as the telescopes seem to indicate it is growing. If Dr. Hoyle's suggestion is taken seriously, then the universe may not have had just one big beginning, when everything that is was created. Instead, the universe can be thought of as creating new parts for itself continually. The universe is still being created.

Then just as a living animal stops growing when it reaches the size that best suits its life, so the universe may stop expanding or growing when it reaches a certain size. There may even be a time when it will begin to grow smaller. Like all living things that men know, the universe may slowly lose its energy and die. If it dies, will it leave a seed of some kind so that a new universe may begin to live and grow? Or can it be that the universe is immortal as men have usually thought of God as being, without any beginning and without any end?

These are some of the exciting ideas that modern scientists are suggesting regarding the beginning and the ending of the universe. Their ideas are really but new questions they are raising for which they hope the scientists of tomorrow may perhaps find some answers. Although the scientists of today have learned a very great deal about the atom, and although they have discovered how to change one kind of atom into another kind that is its closest relative, they have not yet uncovered the mystery still hidden in the atom's nucleus. How then can they understand the far greater mystery of a universe of trillions upon trillions of atoms? And how is it that some atoms that have banded together and are alive in you and in me are able to think and to ask questions about other atoms that whirl and spark millions of miles away?

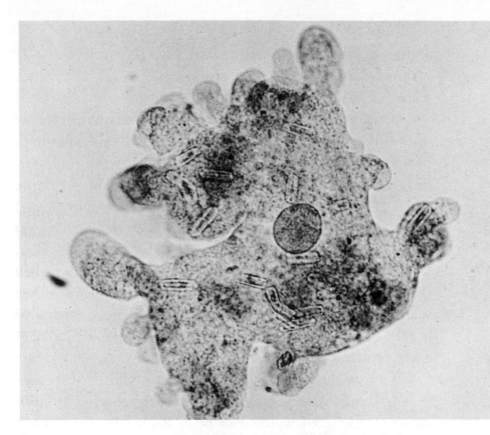

An amoeba greatly magnified. When alive it changes its shape continually.

Beginnings of Plant and Animal Life

Probably this old earth of ours had been spinning its way around the sun year after year for two or more billion years before any kind of living thing could have kept alive on it. Over half of the rock pages of the book of earth are empty of all fossil pictures of living things. It was not until the soft hot rocks had cooled and hardened, and the steaming mists and gases had gathered into oceans, and an envelope of soft warm air had been formed around the world that living things of any kind could survive.

Then at long last somewhere in the shallow seas, or in some quiet pool between the rocks, this wondrous thing happened. Some little light-green specks — so tiny we could not have seen them even if we had been there to look — became alive! These specks were larger and much more complicated than atoms, yet even they were so small they could have been seen only through a microscope. We call them one-celled living things. They were plants, not animals. Perhaps they were much like the tiny green *algae* (al′-jēe), or one-celled plants, you can see today if you look through a microscope at a drop of water from a scummy pond. Perhaps they were even smaller.

Tiny as these first algae were, they could do three important things that no speck of earth or drop of water or bit of air, as far as we know, has ever been able to do. First of all, they could, in some way we do not yet fully understand, gather energy from the sunshine and mingle it with water and air, and change the mixture into food they could eat. This is something that no animal — not even man — is yet able to do. The algae could make their own food in this way because they had inside them a wonder substance called *chlorophyll* (klō′-rō-fil). If these little algae lost their chlorophyll or if they could not be in the sunshine, they died. Since these first one-celled plants could eat, they could also grow. When they grew to be as large as it was good for them to be, they could do a third very remarkable thing. They could grow narrow across the middle and split into two cells. So each little plant could produce another plant just like itself. This power to produce another living thing like oneself, making it out of oneself, we call the power of *reproduction*. Because the algae had this power, they multiplied. One little alga became two, two became four, four became eight, and so on and on until there were probably millions and trillions of algae in the seas.

After a while — we do not know how long — some of these new plants came to be different from their ancestors. Instead of living inside a soft filmy covering, some covered themselves with hard skins which they made by pulling silica out of the water. These coverings were of different shapes — such as stars, triangles, globes, and crystals of many designs. Such one-celled plants as these still abound in our pools and are called diatoms (dī'-a-toms). A good miscroscope and a few drops of water from a sluggish pond are all that is needed to remind one of the first life on the earth perhaps two billion years ago.

This first great change from a piece of earth or drop of water that we usually think of as not alive into something that was alive leaves the scientists still wondering. How could such small bits of life begin? How could they grow to be so beautiful?

The First Animals — the Protozoa

If the algae or diatoms lost their chlorophyll or if perhaps some of them were born without it, they were unable to make their own food out of the energy of the sunshine and bits of air and water. Many probably went hungry and died, but others began to do the only thing they could do and stay alive.

They began eating the other algae that had chlorophyll. In this way they got their food already made for them. These one-celled creatures without chlorophyll we call the first animals or *proto-zo-a* (prō-tō-zō'-a). During all the millions of years since then, all the animal descendants of the first protozoa have been completely dependent on plants to make their food for them. Even man has not learned the secret of this wonder-working chlorophyll.

Some of the first protozoa were soft sprawling transparent bodies that could stretch themselves in any direction, gathering diatoms into their bulging arms and holding them until eaten. These we call *amoebas* (a-mē'-bas). Others became long and thin and grew hairs or cilia along their sides to use as paddles. Others fastened themselves to rocks and grew finger-like bodies with cups on the ends of the fingers. Some of these protozoa even grew shell coverings of many beautiful shapes.

For millions of years, the diatoms and the other algae, and the amoebas and the other protozoa were probably the only living things on earth. No human eye could have seen them except through a microscope. But there were no human eyes and there were no microscopes. There never would have been any larger plants and animals on the earth had not some of these one-celled living things hit upon a new way of living.

The First Many-Celled Living Things

We wonder how one-celled living things, without anything looking like a brain, could have brought about the next important change. Some think it happened by chance. Others think more than chance was needed. Some cells, after splitting in two, stuck together instead of separating. There was probably some advantage in doing so since the bigger plants were not so easily eaten as the littler ones. But it made living more complicated than it had been when each single cell went where it pleased and did all its own work. When the cells clung together in balls or wheels or cords, the cells on the inside could no longer breathe in the food or take it away from the algae. Some cells had to be the food gatherers and the swimmers for the whole group, while other cells had to specialize in the splitting to produce new cells. So the cells had to divide up the work or else all would die. We cannot help marveling at how well so many of them succeeded.

The Wonderfully Successful Volvox

One of the most remarkable of these first many-celled creatures was the *Volvox*. Its descendants today — probably much like their ancient ancestors — can be found in many warm fresh-water lakes, beautiful blue-green balls of living gelatin, half plant, half animal. The scientists have given them the name *Volvox* (which is the Latin word for *roller*) because they revolve when they swim, as if on an axis, and they move in the direction to which the axis points.

A Volvox is about the size of a small grain of sand. Through a microscope, that magnifies one hundred times, it looks like a ball of green emeralds, about the size of a pea. Each cell in the outside circles of cells has two cilia and an "eye spot." These cells do the seeing for the whole Volvox. They also breathe in energy from the sun, air, and water, transform it into food, and pass on enough for the next layer of cells, and even enough to feed the whole Volvox. The outside cells also do the rowing. Those little hairy oars coming in pairs out of all the outside cells do not swish around in just any sort of way. The tiny oarsmen seem to be organized. They row in rhythm as if the beautiful Volvox were their captain.

The cells in the center of the Volvox are the only ones that can reproduce, and they began a new way of doing this. Instead of simply splitting in two like the algae, some of them changed into two kinds of cells. One kind is round like an egg; the other is spindle shaped like a sperm. When the time became ripe, the Volvox made an opening in the underside of its spherical body and down dropped the two kinds of new cells. Before long the egg cell and the sperm cell met and their bodies blended together. A new Volvox had begun its life. The parent Volvox, however, much weakened by the loss of these cells, soon stopped rolling. Slowly its body changed back to the air and water and bits of earth out of which it had been made. The parent Volvox had completed its life. It died.

The algae and the protozoa never really died like this. To reproduce, they simply divided and each half went on living as if new. Each new algae started out exactly like its parent. But when single cells began living together in one body and divided up the work of living, the cells lost their ability to do everything for themselves. No one cell could live long without the others. This meant that when babies were born, the rest of the cells all died together. In the history of living things, dying then became natural and necessary. And the mixing of two different kinds of cells, one male and the other female, in order to reproduce new life, made the evolution of life into higher and higher forms possible. The two

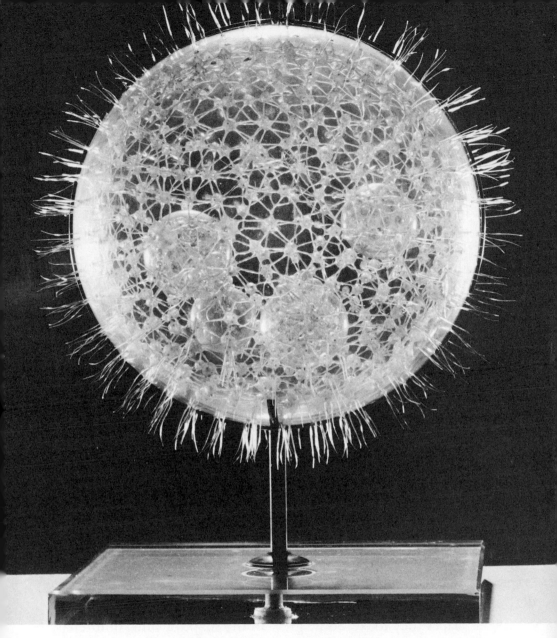

A glass model of a volvox enlarged from its natural size,
which is about that of a grain of sand.

Some of the early forms of life in the sea 500,000,000 years ago.

cells that mated were not exactly alike. Each of them had a slightly different set of patterns or *genes* in it to grow by. When the two sets of genes joined, the new baby animal was likely to grow up to be just a little different from either of its parents.

The Volvox, however, was not the only living thing in those far-off times that became many celled. Once the experiment was begun, there seems to have been no end to the many different ways the cells combined and the many different shapes they took. Some grew in the shape of pink umbrellas, that opened and closed as the animal swam. We call their descendants today *jelly fish*. Some became shaped like tubes. Some fastened themselves to sandy bottoms and grew trunk-like bodies with rows of finger-like feelers around their mouths. They looked so much like flowers that we call their descendants today *sea anemones*. Some became shaped like worms with paddles. Others crawled through the mud by folding themselves and pushing.

Some of these flat worms were born with an even greater addition to their bodies. They grew little lumps at their front ends which were connected with their back ends by very fine threads like telegraph wires. These small lumps were perhaps among the very first real brains; and the fine threads, the first nerves. This means that in the history of life some of the cells in these sea worms had begun to specialize on brain work, while other cells fed them. This was a big gain. The front of the animal had now a better way of sending word back to its hind end, and of letting it know what to do.

The Animals Grow Hard Skins and Shells for Defense

For millions of years the oceans remained warm and the number of plants and animals greatly increased. As the waters became more crowded, the animals began fighting among themselves for food. Some even began the practice of eating other animals as well as algae. Naturally those who found themselves in danger tried to protect themselves.

The sponges spread themselves like bushes over the sea floor, hiding their tender cells inside of thickened tubes. Corals pulled in lime from the waters and built themselves white and pink castles, each cell being quite safe in its small room made of lime. Some animals shut themselves up in shells as the sea urchins and snails do. Some grew shells that were hinged together on one side and could be opened and closed like the oysters and other bivalves of today. Others grew toughened skins, with spines, like those of the starfish. Others built their thick skins in sections like lobsters and shrimps today.

The First Backboned Fish

Three hundred and fifty million years ago most of the sea animals had thus made themselves some kind of armor. They kept hidden inside of thick skins, bony plates, segmented plates, or shells. Yet there were a few that began growing their bony parts on the inside rather than on the outside of their bodies. We call these the first real fish because they had backbones.

Now this backbone is a very remarkable "invention," for it was not simply one stiff bony pole. It was made up of a row of small bones (called *vertebrae*), neatly fitted together and tied to each other by muscles and nerves. Such a backbone, that could be easily bent, made it possible for a fish to swim freely, and at the same time it made the fish stronger and able to swim faster than the soft little worm could ever do. These backboned fish could protect themselves without armor because of their swift swimming. So they multiplied and grew in many different sizes and shapes.

The First Adventurers on Land — the Amphibians

Let us now turn back in our story to ask, "When and how did living things begin to live on land?" How we wish we could know! For changing from a home in the water to a home on dry land was one of the most important steps in this whole story of evolution. If some plants or animals had never done this, all living things would still be swimming in the water.

As the centuries passed, the shapes of the continents and the oceans kept changing. Earthquakes joggled the earth's surface. Wide plains and ocean bottoms were lifted up. New mountains and valleys were formed. Some seas overflowed and deepened. Others became shallow and small. Some no doubt even dried up entirely. Where this happened, the plants and animals in them were stranded. Being unable to breathe air, many died. Yet there were some that succeeded in staying alive. Let us imagine how this might have happened.

The simpler living things, we think, must have been the first to succeed, such as the algae and the protozoa. Let us imagine that some of these one-celled plants and animals were floating together in a thin green scum over the top of some shallow pool near the shore. A brisk wind splashed a wave of water over a rock, and as the wave receded it left the green scum and the plants and animals sprawled over the wet rock. Lying close beside an alga was perhaps a *fungus*. The alga, having chlorophyll, was able to feed directly on the energy of the sunshine if it had at least a little water. The fungus, not having cholorophyll, could not make its own food, but simply by lying close to the alga it could help hold a little water on the rock. At the same time it could pull in a little of the food the alga had in it. So the alga and the fungus could have started a kind of partnership. If they stayed close together, they may have grown together and made the little plant we call a *lichen* (lī'-ken). And the spores (or simple seeds) they bore would have been a combination of alga and fungus.

If you think this story is just a fanciful tale, go out some day to a barren rocky shore where nothing seems to be growing. You will be almost sure to find here and there some gray-green carpets spread out on the rocks. Look at these through a microscope and you will see just such lichen cups, made of little gray fungi and little green algae, grown together as we have imagined they may have done millions of years ago.

Perhaps some of the other one-celled animals also may have been washed up on the rocks — amoebas or flat worms with brains. They probably fed on some of these gray-green pastures of lichen, but the lichen multiplied in spite of their enemies. Some of the larger animals perhaps were able to crawl over the rocks and some even may have gotten back into the water. Many of the backboned fish that were washed ashore probably died. Some, however, that already had small air bags along with gills, could breathe air for a while. Some of the fish began growing lungs instead of gills. As the years passed more fish with lungs instead of gills were born. Some began using their fins for crawling. Later some were born with fins that looked quite like feet and were fastened strongly to their backbones.

These first animals that were able to live for a while on land probably went back into the water to lay their eggs. The young that hatched in the water began their lives as fish. Just as polliwogs do today, they grew in the water, then slowly changed their shapes. They grew legs and lungs and crawled out onto the land to live their lives, returning to the water only to lay their eggs. These animals we call *amphibians,* which means they could live both on land and in the water.

In the meantime the plants of the sea had been multiplying fast. Many had grown to immense sizes, as seaweeds of many varieties, some living entirely under the water, others partly above the surface. They reproduced themselves by means of *spores* — small seeds that clung to the leaves and branches but that were easily blown away. Many of these spores were dropped in the marshes along the shores where they took root and thrived. The air was muggy and warm and the marshes stretched endlessly. Slowly the seaweeds crept farther and farther from the water. As they did so, their shapes and sizes changed till the time came when miles and miles of bare rocks were covered with green ferns and rushes and even with trees. Some were leafless; some were like our pines of today. Many trees grew to great heights, even to fifty or sixty feet. (Man is still burning coal made from the buried trunks of these ancient trees.)

The warm marshy lands must have often tempted the sea animals toward the shore because of the very abundant and easy food supply they offered. They probably lured especially the slow-moving and sluggish ones, such as the scorpions and segmented worms. These amphibians, however, took only small risks. They kept close to the shore for they could not give up laying their eggs in the water. The animals that were to reach greatness on land had to be more adventurous.

The Age of the Great Reptiles — the Dinosaurs

These were the animals that found ways of living out of the water all the time. They grew thick skins so that cells inside their bodies did not easily dry out. They even gave up the habit of going back to the water to lay their eggs. Instead, they surrounded their eggs with shells as the birds do, and left them in the warm moist sand to hatch, so that their young never knew what it felt like to be fish and swim in the water. These animals we call *reptiles*.

In the widespread swampy jungles, the reptiles had food enough and to spare. Big and little reptiles grew side by side. Some like small lizards and toads crawled or hopped around. Giant turtles, wide as a barn door, crawled over the logs. Others jumped on two feet like featherless ostriches with perky tails.

The most fantastic of the reptiles were the *dinosaurs* or giant lizards, whose skeletons are on exhibit in many museums. No teller of fairy tales has imagined giants more amazing. Some of the dinosaurs had long sharp bird-like bills, yet with two hundred teeth inside them. Some had huge collars that lay back of their eyes like shields; some had horns on their heads like the rhinoceros, while others had their horns on their tails. Some had strong armor plates, lying like flat saucers all over their backs, while others had their armor sticking up straight like an Indian war bonnet of bones instead of feathers.

The so-called king of all the dinosaurs, *Tyrannosaurus,* stood twenty feet high as he rested his heavy body on his strong tail. He had hind feet with claws like an eagle's and two small front feet like a kangaroo's. With one lash of his claws and a few bites with his sharp teeth, he could make quick end of almost any other animal.

Nevertheless, *Tyrannosaurus* had many rivals, some of whom were even bigger than he, although not so dangerous to meet. One of these, the *Brontosaurus,* had thick elephant-like feet and a long snake-like neck and head. With an easy lift of his long neck he could gather his breakfast from the

A painting of two of the giant dinosaurs, the Tyrannosaurus
and the Triceratops.

topmost branches of the tree ferns. He was a slow old fellow,
however, with a small brain, who went lumbering through
the swamps, wading with his awkward bow legs through the
mud.

The dinosaurs — the biggest and mightiest animals that
ever lived on land — had their way for one hundred and
fifty million years. If you measured the time since the first
man lived on the earth as being like a half-inch, you would
have to make a line almost six feet long for the years that
the dinosaurs prospered and had their way. For some reason
which the scientists cannot yet explain, all the dinosaurs died
out. Only their skeletons and fossilized eggs and giant footprints remain to tell their story.

One of the huge reptiles that turned into a bird. It is named *archaeopterix*, which means "ancient bird." Note the claws on its wings and the teeth in its mouth.

The First Adventurers into the Air

While the giant dinosaurs were still fighting in the swampy jungles, many smaller animals shared the land with them. Some of these kept to the ground and hid from the ravenous dinosaurs in the mud and rushes.

Others of these smaller animals had grown wings and had learned to fly. Some scientists think that the ancestors of present-day insects were flying long before any of the dinosaurs had been born. The first insects to fly were descended from the segmented worms and scorpions and their like. Perhaps, like dragon flies, they first learned to flit over the surface of

TIME SCALE	ERAS	DURATION OF PERIODS	PERIODS		DOMINANT ANIMAL LIFE
			Quaternary	Recent Pleistocene	Man
10 20 30 40 50 60 70	CENOZOIC 70 MILLION YEARS DURATION	70	Tertiary	EPOCHS: Pliocene Miocene Oligocene Eocene Paleocene	Mammals
80 90 100	MESOZOIC	60	Cretaceous		
150		35	Jurassic		
200	120 MILLION YEARS DURATION	35	Triassic		Dinosaurs
		30	Permian		
250		25	Pennsylvanian		
		25	Mississippian		Primitive Reptiles
300	PALEOZOIC	40	Devonian		Amphibians
350		30	Silurian		Fishes
400		70	Ordovician		
450		80	Cambrian		Invertebrates
500	−350 MILLION YEARS DURATION				
Figures in millions of years	PROTEROZOIC		2500+ MILLION YEARS DURATION		BEGINNINGS OF LIFE
	ARCHAEOZOIC				

A diagram showing the most important steps in the evolution of life, and the millions of years each lasted.

the water. Fossils of butterflies and huge dragon flies have been found alongside the bones of dinosaurs.

Many thousand years later, some of the lighter and smaller dinosaurs also took to flying. They grew bat-like wings and long beaks. Their hip bones grew smaller, and they lost their tails. Their hind limbs became short and thin.

Then before the rule of the dinosaurs had ended, real birds with feathers appeared. Instead of being cold blooded as the dinosaurs were and all fish are, these birds were warm blooded and had fast-beating hearts. In the Chicago Museum of Natural History is a model of one of these first birds. Its name is *Archeopteryx* (Ar-kē-op'-ter-ix), a long name meaning merely ancient bird. It flew 135,000,000 years ago. The claws in its wings are tell-tale signs of its reptile ancestors.

Mammals with Milk for Their Young

At last the power of the dinosaurs came to an end. With their dying out, we turn over another of earth's stone pages, and in place of giants we find little animals like rats, opossums, small kangaroos, anteaters, weasels, and even moles become important. The weak seem to have had the power to survive when the strong failed.

All these animals had certain new qualities which the reptiles never gained. First of all, they all had warm fur coats to keep them warm. And even more remarkable was the new way they had of caring for their babies. Instead of laying eggs and dropping them in the sand and leaving them to lie unguarded, the mothers kept the eggs of their young inside their own bodies until the young were well formed and had their own fur. Then the babies were born. Some babies, like those of the opossums and the kangaroos of today, were born half

developed, but the mother animal put the newborn immediately into a pocket of fur she had in the under part of her
body. There she kept it warm and with her. The little animal
could drink from its mother's nipples whenever it chose. Not
until it was fully formed was it allowed to go free.

Such milk glands or mammary glands were something
new in the world. All mothers in this group of animals have
these glands and this is why they are called *mammals*. Milk
glands are one of Nature's very important inventions. It has
meant that newly born mammal babies have to stay close to
their mothers during the early weeks or months where the
mothers can watch and protect and feed them. One result is
that the mammal mothers often grow to like their babies, and
the babies become fond of their mothers. Some scientists think
this is the way mother-child love had its beginnings.

As the ages passed, the mammals increased in number
and in variety. Some of them came to have larger brains than
the others. Some, like the mammoths and bison, were covered
with thick shaggy coats of fur. The more fleet-footed ones
— such as the saber-toothed tigers, the reindeer, and the horses
— kept themselves warm with thinner coats of fur.

During perhaps fifty million years, mammals of many
kinds developed and prospered on the earth. Some like the
horses grew from being the size of dogs until they became as
large as our present-day horses. Other mammals have not
changed at all during the millions of years — such as the opossums and the kangaroos.

As in all the other parts of this story of evolution, the
passing of the years has meant for some animals much changing and improving; for others it has meant always doing and
always being just like their ancestors.

Beginnings of Human Life

At last we reach the question about which we are all most curious. When did the first human beings begin to live on the earth? And what were they like? The scientists tell us that we are blood relatives of all the animals that have ever lived, from the protozoa to the apes. We are not descended from the kind of apes that live today, but we and these apes of today are both descended from a kind of ape that lived about twenty million years ago.

Sometimes people say jokingly that we are descended from monkeys. Since this is not what the scientists believe, it is well for us to understand why it is an incorrect statement. Monkeys and apes are very different kinds of animals. Monkeys are always small and they have long tails and usually walk on four feet. Apes are usually larger, they have no tails to speak of, and they often walk on two feet. Apes are more like human beings in the shape of their skeletons and in the size of their brains than any other animal. Many years ago apes were living on all the continents. Today they are found wild only in Asia and Africa. There are only four species of apes today: the *chimpanzee* and *gorilla* in Africa, and the *orang-utan* and *gibbon* in Asia. The apes of today are all tree dwellers.

Twenty million years ago, probably all apes were tree

This is how one artist has imagined one of our ape ancestors might have looked about 20,000,000 years ago.

dwellers, although not so skilled in swinging from branch to branch or from tree to tree as is the gibbon today. Nor were they as large and strong as the gorilla. Then there came a time (so it is believed) when the apes separated into two groups. This happened perhaps because the climate of much of Europe and Asia changed. Where once there had been dense tropical forests filled with fruit-bearing trees, now there were treeless hills covered with snow for many months in the year.

Threatened with starvation, some of the apes risked coming down from the trees to live. They learned to hunt for other kinds of food on the ground. The apes who stayed in the trees gradually developed more and more skill as branch swingers and jumpers. Their forelegs turned into long arms with long-fingered hands that could hold fast to the branches. Their hind legs remained short, and they never developed heels and arches in their feet like those of man. These apes who stayed in the trees did not become the ancestors of man. They are the ancestors of the chimpanzee, the gorilla, the orang-utan, and the gibbon.

It was the apes who came down from the trees to live mostly on the ground that changed the most, and became the ancestors of man. Instead of reaching for fruit high on branches above their heads, they had to learn to dig in the ground, to catch rabbits and moles or to lift stones to find insects and grubs. Living on land was more dangerous than living in trees. Larger animals were continually scouting for smaller ones. The apes had to learn to move quickly. If they stood up straight they could see danger coming, so they slowly grew ankles and heels in their feet so that they could walk upright. Their brains grew larger too because they used them more. These apes that began to learn how to live on land were the ones whose descendants millions of years later were to become human beings.

A few years ago a company of explorers in North Africa discovered the skull and parts of the skeleton of an ape which they decided must have lived over twenty million years ago. The bones in his hands and feet looked much like human bones. Apparently he was beginning to walk erect on two feet, but his brain and the shape of his head still seemed like those of the usual ape. An imaginative artist painted a picture of the ape that might have had these bones in his body. The painting hangs in the British Museum of Natural History in London. Since this ape was beginning to be a little different from the apes and a little like a man, he has been called the common ancestor, both of mankind and of the apes of today, the chimpanzee, the gorilla, the orang-utan, and the gibbon.

The First Half-Men and Half-Apes

Some of the most interesting discoveries that have been made in this long search for man's ancestors have started almost by accident. Recent finds made in South Africa, a few miles northwest of Johannesburg, were like that. Men who were mining for lime had been dynamiting a cliff near by. The explosion opened up a cave that had clearly once been lived in. A chunk of rock was hurled at the feet of a geologist standing by. He picked up the stone, and to his amazement he found himself looking at what seemed like "the toothy grin of a child's skull." Or was it the skull of a chimpanzee? Its good forehead and teeth seemed like those of a child, but its nose and jaws looked like those of an ape.

Other explorers became interested. Caves in other rocks and crevices nearby were explored. Other skulls were dug up of full-grown individuals. The explorers found also the bones of animals, antelopes, and baboons, and even those of a saber-toothed tiger. They noticed that the skulls of all of these animals had been shattered as if by a hard blow. Why was this? One of the men experimented to find out. He picked up the thigh bone of an antelope that lay nearby. He struck one of the unbroken skulls with it and found he had made exactly the same kind of dent and crush in the skull that was in all the other skulls in the cave. He concluded that these apes, or men (whichever they were), who had lived probably a million years ago, had been bright enough to use a thigh bone as a killing tool. No ape has ever been known to do such a thing. Were these apes that lived perhaps a million years ago half-apes and half-men?

The scientists learned other exciting things when they studied the skeletons of these African ape men, and they concluded that the ape men could have been well able to stand erect. Their hands were human in shape and their teeth also, yet they were mere pygmies in size; and their skulls could have held brains but little larger than a chimpanzee's. Finally one item tipped the scales in favor of their being half-human. It was this: Remains of fires were found in the caves alongside the bones. Apparently these ape-men had learned to use fire. Wild animals, even apes, run from fire, or they shy away and leave it alone. Surely these cave dwellers deserved the title *African Ape Men,* for they had had the brains to use a thigh bone as a tool and the courage to experiment with fire and to use it to make living more comfortable and safer.

We may well honor the first of our inventive ancestors who made friends with fire.

The Giant Men of Java Who Walked Erect

It was probably a volcanic eruption that buried the body of the *Java Man* over five hundred thousand years ago. It is thought that the island of Java was at that time linked to the Malay Peninsula by a land bridge. Possibly these early men of Java had migrated down from India or from some other part of Asia during the first Ice Age to enjoy the tropical warmth, and to find plentiful food. A number of other fossilized skulls and skeletons have been found on the island, alongside giant turtles, tapirs, and hyenas. These Java Men apparently were well able to stand erect and they were good hunters. Perhaps their most striking feature was their size. Some of them must have been giants seven or eight feet tall, but their brains were not large in comparison with their size. It is interesting to find evidence of there being giants near the beginning of mankind's history, for so many legends about giants in the long ago have been told. Even the Bible tells of giants in the days just after the flood.

The Peking Men of Dragon Bone Hill

An even more exciting discovery was made in North China about forty miles from Peking. The bones were found in an immense cave in the limestone hillside called "Dragon Bone Hill." The clue that led finally to the decision to dig into this hillside came from the discovery that for centuries

The first Java men may have looked something like this.

Chinese druggists had been selling so-called "dragons' bones" to be used as medicine. The bones were pounded into powder and sold in bottles. The larger the bone had been, the stronger the medicine. Where had these bones been gotten? What were these dragons — mammoths, dinosaurs, or men? These were questions the visiting scientists were asking. No one thirty years ago knew of any bones having been found on "Dragon Bone Hill," but why the name? The story is a long one — twenty years long, in fact. We can give only the last chapter here.

A group of men, coming from a number of western countries, began digging into "Dragon Bone Hill." What a wealth of relics they found! But they were not the bones of dinosaurs or mammoths, but the bones of ancient men! The explorers collected parts of forty to eighty human skeletons and hundreds of teeth belonging to persons who must have been living over half a million years ago. Thousands of tools lay scattered about — hammer stones, choppers, flint scrapers, and knives. There were also tools made from bones, and hundreds of skeleton remains of goats, wild boars, hyenas, brown bears, dogs, wolves, foxes, leopards, horses, bison, and antlered deer in great abundance.

Other caves in the hills nearby were explored. Ruins of hearthstones were found where the ashes still lay from many a glowing fire. It was clear that these early *Peking Men* had found roast meat much tastier and easier to chew than raw flesh. Although it is unpleasant to report, signs were also found to show that these early ancestors of humanity were sometimes cannibals.

Not so big bodied as the *Men of Java,* these *Peking Men* had larger brains. They were no doubt able to talk to each other. They lived and hunted in large family groups. What finally happened to them is still an unsolved mystery.

The Neanderthal Man

About the same time that *Peking Men* were prospering in Asia another race or type of men appeared in Europe, called the *Neanderthal Men,* named from the town in Germany near which their fossil bones were first found. Short in stature, but robust and energetic, they spread over most of Europe's livable sections. Much of Europe was cold during the thousands of years these *Neanderthalers* roamed the land. Great glaciers were formed in the mountains. The winters were long and the short summers rainy. These early men had to be rugged and daring. When days were warm they probably slept out in the open. But when the cold winds swept through the valleys and the snow covered the ground, the shelter of big rocks was not enough. They searched out caves in the cliffs where they could be protected. The animals about them had heavy fur coats to keep them warm, but men had merely toughened skins, slightly covered with hair. They had to invent ways to clothe themselves in the skins of the animals they slew. This called for a new tool, a sharp flint scraper that could clean all rotting flesh from the fur. To cure a piece of fur is nothing simple or easy. The Neanderthalers learned to flake pieces of flint, by studying how the flint was made. The old must have taught these skills to the young. To do these things, they must have been able to talk in words. Little by little our ancestors were learning.

The Neanderthal Men became skilled and courageous hunters. They had to be in order to compete with such fearsome animals as the saber-toothed tiger, the cave bear, the woolly rhinoceros, and the hairy mammoth. These Neanderthal people lived and loved, their children were born and

A bear invades the cave of a Neanderthal man and woman.

their old folks died, generation after generation, for a hundred thousand years and more. They became a great people, outnumbering all others of the human race in Europe, Africa, and the Middle East. Neanderthal Men were clearly no morons, the average brain among them being almost equal in size to that of modern man. As they became more skilled in hunting, they needed to spend less time hunting. When they had learned to cook their food, they needed to spend less time chewing and eating it. So little by little these ancestors of man had more and more leisure. With more leisure they began to do more thinking, and also a new kind of thinking.

Evidence of this was shown the scientists when they discovered a new thing they had not found in Java or in Peking. This new thing was that the Neanderthalers began burying their dead carefully and with a little ceremony. In front of some of their caves, graves have been found in which the dead body had been carefully laid down, with tools or ornaments placed neatly beside it.

We wonder what their thoughts were when they worked out this new way of doing. Did they think their relatives were still alive after death — even though invisible? Were they giving them goodby gifts to take with them wherever it was they were going? Were their feelings and wonderings like ours? Are we not still asking what being dead means? We can't help but like our Neanderthal ancestors for trying to do something special at so important a time.

The Cro-Magnon Man — Homo Sapiens (Man, the Wise)
    "A mystery people" from somewhere in Asia or Africa about twenty or thirty thousand years B.C. migrated into

The model of a cave where Cro-Magnon artists etched and
painted their rock pictures 20,000 years ago.

Europe. Some say they fought their way into the continent, driving out or killing the Neanderthalers. Others believe that they were lured by the prospects of good hunting, and that as they moved slowly into the hunting grounds of the Neanderthalers, they competed with them for the food. Being more skilled, and quicker in their movements than the Neanderthalers, they increased in numbers. They and the Neanderthalers probably intermarried, and slowly the Neanderthalers as such died out.

The name *Cro-Magnon* was given these new people because it is the name of the locality in France near which their fossil skeletons were first found. In their bodily make-up they were just like men of today in every important way. Many of them were tall and thin (some being six feet tall), and their skulls held brains as large as those of the average man of today.

The Cro-Magnon people had learned all the skills the Neanderthalers had acquired and had added to them. They chipped their flint stones with even more skill and purpose, and so they had a larger variety of tools. They also worked with bones and ivory. They made needles even, so that they could sew their fur pieces together. They also made buttons of bone with which they buttoned their clothes. Pieces of ivory tusks, beautifully carved with designs of animals and plants, have been found in their caves. Their caves have been discovered in England, Belgium, France, and Spain.

Although they did not invent a way to write their thoughts, they were amazingly skilled in painting them. It is for their cave paintings and etchings that the Cro-Magnon people are best known today. The first discovery of these

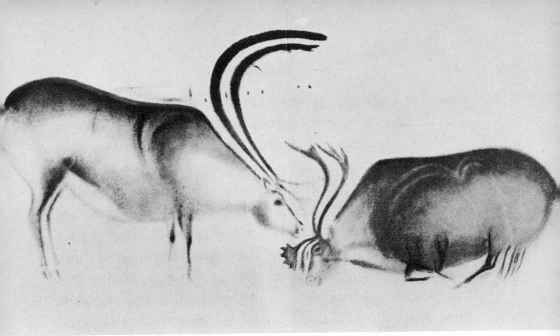

Two wild deer talking together. Painted in color by a Cro-
Magnon artist in the cave near Font-de-Gaume, France.

caves about one hundred years ago is a thrilling story. To
think that any adventurous traveler today in France or Spain
can see for himself pictures of hundreds of bison, mammoths,
reindeer, bears, and horses — the work of primitive hunters
living twenty thousand years ago!

Why did they choose the darkest caves for these paintings
— the ones farthest back in the sides of the mountains? How
did they work in the darkness? Why did they etch and paint
so many animal pictures, some with spears piercing the animals' sides? How did they learn to make paints out of pow-
dered stones, mixed with fat or the white of birds' eggs? Did
they paint with their fingers, or with pieces of fur tied to
sticks? Did they etch the hard stones with pointed flints?
How did they light the caves in order to do the painting?
What spurred them to become so inventive? Who were the
teachers? Why did they paint pictures now and then of men

dressed in animal skins and animal heads? Many such questions the cave explorers have been asking and trying to answer.

It is now quite well agreed upon by the men who have been studying these matters that the caves with the paintings were not the homes of these primitive men. They were their shrines or places of prayer, we might say. There was no one to teach them how to pray. They had to work things out for themselves as best they could. They were beginning to think about more things than those they could see. Perhaps they had thoughts such as these: "It is dangerous to live alongside these big wild animals. Something more than spears and clubs is needed if we are to keep alive. There are spirits inside these animals — just as there are spirits inside us. We must capture the spirits of the animals as well as the animals themselves."

"These pictures we've painted look alive, don't they? That's because we caught the spirit of the animal. It's held fast in the painting. It can't hurt us now. The animal whose spirit it is will feel weak without it. If in our hunting we find him, we will be able to kill."

"How foolish!" some may perhaps say. "These cave men believed in magic." That is true. We know that magic doesn't work. We know that pictures of animals are not alive. But these men who were just beginning to think had not yet found out that magic won't work. They were experimenting with things they did not understand. But even though the magic did not work, something else did work. Perhaps a band of men about to go hunting would gather in one of these cave shrines, and by the light of crude torches would look at the

pictures of animals already pierced with spears or animals running from their homes. They shouted perhaps, feeling almost
as if they were already bringing home their prey. It is thought
that probably these primitive hunters often acted out a hunt
right there in the cave, running and throwing their spears even
at their paintings, or into their sculptured animals in clay.
When the hunters had finished their dancing, they were able
to go forth to the dangerous hunt with added courage and
confidence.

These are but guesses at the feelings and thoughts of these
early people. They have left us no written records to tell what
they were trying to say in their pictures. We can be sure of
one thing, however: They were doing the best they knew and
they tried very hard to make their work their best. We honor
them for their boldness in experimenting, and we marvel at
the artistic skills they attained.

This then is the story, briefly told, of the beginnings of
life up to the time when living beings who can well be called
men and women lived on the earth. No storyteller of long
ago could have imagined a fanciful tale of the beginning of
human life on the earth half as full of wonder and mystery
as is this story of evolution. There are still many gaps in the
story to be filled in. There are probably parts that will always
be beyond the power of men to understand. We are left with
more questions unanswered than we probably even thought
to ask in the beginning.

And what of the future? Is man superior to all the other
animals? We cannot shed our skins like the snakes, nor can
we roll ourselves up in a cocoon blanket and like the caterpil-

lar make ourselves wings. We cannot run like a deer, nor have we the strength of an elephant or a lion. We do not have the beautiful skin of the tiger, nor can we fly with the ease and grace of an eagle. In what ways is man superior? Will he be superior a million years from now? Is the evolution of life going to stop with humanity as it now is? Will it ever stop? What can we do so that our children and our grandchildren may be superior to us?

Some Wonderings of Our Own

We have been asking very large questions. How did everything begin? We have asked how did man begin? We have asked how did our earth begin, how did our solar system begin, how did our galaxy begin? And we have even asked how did *all* galaxies and *all* suns and *all* worlds begin?

We have read the answers given in story form by different people from different lands and different times. We have asked both the primitive people of long ago and the scientists of today. It has been a stirring adventure. We understand now how other people have felt. We see why they thought as they did, and we know why the scientists keep asking more and more questions. For like Kofi in Africa, we too can "go on thinking and thinking and never stop."

But let us come back to some of the smaller questions. How did *you* and *I* begin? How will *we* end, or will *we* ever end? These intimate questions about ourselves may have been waiting quietly all this time behind the big questions.

When then did *you* begin? Ten years ago? Fifteen years ago, did you say? Do you mean you began to be *you* the day you were born? How can that be? Did you not begin nine months before you were born? Does not the thought start a wondering in your mind? Nine months before you were born, you were a small one-celled gelatin-like ball of life —

not as big as the period at the end of this sentence. Was that speck *you*? How could *you* come out of that? It took mankind as a race about two billion years to evolve from one-celled protozoa into people. How is it *you* could make such a big change from a small one-celled animal into a human baby with billions and billions of cells in your body in so short a time as nine months?

The answer is that your one-celled beginning had in it something that the first protozoa did not have. It had already in it at the start a much larger number of patterns to grow by. Those patterns were strung together in tiny strings inside your one-celled egg. The biologists call these patterns *genes* (jēēns). Very wonderful microscopic pieces of *life* these genes are! For they had in them all the patterns your egg needed to grow by in order to grow into *you*. It is a mystery how these very tiny specks can hold such patterns and how they make the egg follow the patterns. It is as if these little genes could talk and say: "You are to be a boy with brown eyes and dark hair and dark skin," or just the opposite, whichever was needed to make *you*. Yet who ever heard of a one-celled living thing talking?

Probably in that long-ago time, when there were no living animals except the tiny one-celled protozoa, each of these tiny living things had at least one of those wondrous genes inside its cell. It needed something to show it how to be even just another protozoa. But your tiny egg, that began growing inside your mother's body, needed thousands of patterns or genes to grow by if it was to know how to grow and grow in order to become *you*.

And where, we ask, did that little speck of *life*, that was your egg in the beginning, get those patterns to grow by? They came from two germ cells, one a male cell from your father's body and the other a female cell from your mother's body. When you were *conceived* (nine months before you were born), those two cells blended together into one cell — into the beginning of *you*.

And where, we ask, did your father and mother get those small containers of *life* that could join together to make *you*? Again it is hard to imagine (but the scientists have good reasons for believing it). These thousands of special kinds of genes that were needed to make *you* had been kept alive ever since your father and your mother themselves were single cells inside their mothers.

And how did your father and your mother get their genes that told their eggs how to grow? From their four parents, that is, from your grandparents. And where did your grandparents get their genes to grow by? From their parents, that is, from your great-grandparents. And where did your great-grandparents get their genes? How far back must we go to find your very first beginning? We cannot stop, can we, until we have reached the very first living things that were in the beginning of time. Had not these living things lived in the long, long line of ancestors before you, the small egg that began to be *you* would never have known how to become *you*. For it was from them that your egg had slowly gathered the patterns it had for making *you*. It was because millions and millions of years ago male and female creatures began joining their different kinds of germ cells together that *you* began, rather than an *amoeba*. Each new baby creature that was born was a little different from its parents, and some began trying out new ways of doing things. After a while these new ways became firm habits, so firm that new patterns were given to the new eggs to grow by.

The writers of the old Bible had an interesting way to report how persons have been connected with the people before them. They used a word which we seldom use now: *begat*. It means *brought into being*. For example, we read in the Bible: "Abraham begat Isaac, and Isaac begat Jacob, and Jacob begat Judah, etc." So we might describe your connections with those who have lived before you in this way. But we must think of large groups of living things as if they were one single living thing in order to keep your very long story short enough to tell. So this, we might say, is the story of the beginning of *You*.

The *Protozoa* begat the *Volvox*. The *Volvox* begat the *Worm with Brains*. The *Worm with Brains* begat the *Fish*. The *Fish* begat the *Amphibian*. The *Amphibian* begat the *Reptile*. The *Reptile* begat the *Mammal*. The *Mammal* begat the *Ape*. The *Ape* begat *Man*. And *Man* begat *You*.

These are the chapter titles in the long, long story of *You*. We feel the wonder of it, but who can explain it? In some way, something in all these kinds of living creatures is still living in you, and in every person now alive. You — or a part of you — are much, much older than you seem. You feel young. You look young. You have no memory of the ages before you were born. Yet you brought with you on your birthday some tell-tale signs that you already had inside of you a number of patterns to grow by. The millions of cells in your baby body knew how to do thousands of things you have never consciously thought about. Their ancestor cells had gotten used to doing these things "without thinking" thousands of years before you were born. You belong in a living chain, a spiral millions of years old and millions of people and animals long.

And will some of these patterns-to-grow-by that are in you go on living in your children and in your children's children after your body dies? Surely, we cannot imagine this living chain as ending with you. What kinds of patterns for growing will you and your mate be passing on to your children? Can you do anything about improving these patterns? How?

The past has been long. The future may be even longer. We began this book with questions. We close with other and harder questions still unanswered.

Something began me
and it had no beginning;
Something will end me
and it has no end.

CARL SANDBURG*

*From *The People, Yes,* by Carl Sandburg, copyright, 1936, by Harcourt, Brace and Co., Inc.

Personal Acknowledgments

We are indebted to so many friends and scholars — many unknown to us personally — for assistance in gathering these stories from the world's cultures that it would be impossible to name them. All that is possible is to express our gratitude to a few who have given us specific help in person recently.

Without the sponsorship and guidance of the staff of the Division of Education of the Council of Liberal Churches, the book might never have been written. Dr. Ernest W. Kuebler, the head of the Division, and the other editors of curricular materials, Dr. Lucile Lindberg, Mrs. Edith Hunter, and Dr. Robert L'H. Miller, and Mr. Adolphus Cheek, chairman of the Curriculum Committee, and all its members have read at least parts of the manuscript and criticized and discussed many problems with us.

Teachers and parents who have guided groups of boys and girls in an exploring venture through the use of the two former volumes, *Beginnings of Earth and Sky* and *Beginnings of Life and Death,* of which this volume is a combination and revision, have shared with us their enthusiasm and some of their experiences. These reports have helped us more than these friends can ever know by giving us concrete proofs of some of the rich possibilities in this kind of introductory approach for boys and girls to an awareness of the universality of mankind's religious search.

In the writing of the one important new story, not included in the older volumes — the story from the Sumerians and Babylonians — we are happily indebted to Dr. E. A. Speiser, Professor of Oriental Studies and Semitics in the School of Graduate Studies of the University of Pennsylvania, first for his kind permission to use his translation of *The Seven Tablets of Creation,* and also for his suggestions for the improvement of our shortened and simplified version of the story.

In writing the first part of the scientists' story, dealing with the beginnings of the earth and sky, we are deeply grateful to Dr. Harlow Shapley, Professor of Astronomy and Director of the Astronomical Observatory of Harvard University, for reading the manuscript to catch inadvertent errors. We are equally grateful to Dr. Sanborn C. Brown, Professor of Physics at the Massachusetts

Institute of Technology, for not merely reading and commenting on the manuscript but correcting it in three successive versions. Dr. Charles R. Gadaire, Professor of Zoology at International College, Springfield, Massachusetts, generously gave us the initial help by reading the story as it had been told in the former volumes.

In writing the second and third sections of the scientists' story, we are indebted to Dr. Theodosius Dobzhansky, Professor of Genetics at Columbia University, for his reading and criticisms of two successive versions of the story. We gladly acknowledge also the careful study of the manuscript made by Dr. Reginald D. Manwell, Professor of Zoology at Syracuse University, together with his concrete suggestions. We realize we have been extraordinarily privileged in having such personal help from these scholarly specialists.

A number of authors have also contributed unknowingly to our knowledge and insights, far too many even to list. One of these, however, we want to mention by name: Dr. Joseph Wood Krutch, author of *The Great Chain of Life*. Our story of the Volvox is taken largely from his writing. The idea of condensing the ages of evolution into a short series of "begats" is also from him. And he gave us something more difficult to describe but much more important. By his probing beyond the traditional explanations for the process of evolution, he opened our eyes to the true bond that relates us to all living things — the mystery of being alive.

We wish also to express our grateful indebtedness to Gobin Stair, art editor for the Beacon Press, for the devoted care he has taken in preparing the manuscript for publication and most especially for his contribution to the book of six original samples of his own creative art.

Sophia L. Fahs
Dorothy T. Spoerl

Major Sources for the Stories

For the Bushman Story

Stow, George W. *The Native Races of South Africa.* New York, The Macmillan Co., 1910, pp. 130-134.

Frobenius, Leo, and Fox, Douglas C. *African Genesis.* New York, Stackpole Sons, pp. 49-51.

Dornan, S. S. *Pigmies and Bushmen of the Kalahari.* London, Seeley, Service and Co., Ltd., 1925.

For the Story from Australia

Smith, W. Ramsey. *Myths and Legends of the Australian Aboriginals.* London, George Harrap and Co., 1930, Chap. I.

For the Iroquois Indian Story

Barbeau, C. M. *Anthropological Series.* Memoir 80, No. 11. Ottawa, Canada, Government Bureau, 1951.

For the Story from China

Werner, E. T. C. *Myths and Legends of China.* London, George Harrap and Co., 1922, Chap. III.

Ferguson, J. C. *Mythology of All Races,* Vol. VIII. Boston, Marshall Jones Co., 1928, pp. 52-58.

For the Story from Japan

Davis, Frederick Hadland. *Myths and Legends of Japan.* London, George Harrap and Co., 1912.

Masahari, Anesaki. *Mythology of All Races,* Vol. VIII. Boston, Marshall Jones Co., 1928, pp. 221-227.

For the Story from Iceland

Sturluson, Snorri. *The Prose Edda,* trans. by I. A. Blackwell. Stockholm, Norroena Society, 1907.

McCulloch, Canon John A., ed. *Mythology of All Races,* Vol. II. Boston, Marshall Jones Co., 1930, Chap. 33.

For the Story from Sumeria and Babylonia

Pritchard, J. B., ed. *Ancient Near Eastern Texts. Relating to the Old Testament.* Princeton, Princeton University Press, 1950.

E. A. Speiser, translator of the text of the *Seven Tablets of Creation.*

Heidel, Alexander. *The Babylonian Genesis,* 2nd ed. Chicago, Chicago University Press, 1952.

For the Two Stories from Palestine

The Jewish-Christian Bible. Genesis, Chaps. 1, 2, and 3.

For the Story from the Maya Indians

Alexander, Hartley B. Mythology of All Races, Vol. XI. Boston, Marshall Jones Co., 1920, pp. 159-177. Contains extensive selections from an English translation of the Popul Vuh.

Spence, Lewis. Popular Studies in Mythology, Romance, and Folklore, No. 16. London, David Nutt, Ltd., 1908.

For the Miwok Indian Story from California

Powers, Stephen. Tribes of California. Washington, U.S. Government Printing Office, 1877, Chap. 33.

Kroeber, A. L. The Religion of the Indians of California. Berkeley, University of California Publications in American Archaeology. Vol. IV, No. 6, 1907.

For the Wintu Indian Story from California

Curtin, Jeremiah. Creation Myths of Primitive America. Boston, Little, Brown and Co., 1898, pp. 163-174.

For the Two Stories from Greece

Gray, Louis H., ed. The Mythology of All Races, Vol. I. Boston, Marshall Jones Co., 1916.

Gayley, Charles M. The Classic Myths in English Literature. Boston, Ginn and Co., 1904.

For the Zuni Indian Story

Cushing, Frank H. Outline of Zuni Creation Myths. Washington, Smithsonian Institution, Thirteenth Annual Report of American Bureau of Ethnology, 1891-1892.

For the Stories from the Scientists

Since so many books were read in order to write the scientific stories, and since all of these books are recent publications, available in most public libraries, they are listed in the bibliography that follows.

Sources for the Illustrations

5. A Bushman family in the Kalahari Desert, South Africa. A statue by Malvina Hoffman. (Courtesy of the Chicago Museum of Natural History.)

7. A rock painting done by African Bushmen many centuries ago. (Courtesy of the Museum of Modern Art, New York City.)

8. All sorts of animals came forth. A drawing by Gobin Stair.

13. Australian Aborigines are skilled in throwing their long spears. (Courtesy of the American Museum of Natural History.)

14. A present-day Aborigine paints a picture of one of the spirits to whom he prays. (Reproduced from *Brown Men and Red Sand,* by C. P. Mountford, London: Phoenix House, Ltd., 1950.)

23. The first sunset. A drawing by Gobin Stair.

26. Iroquois Indian villagers gathering and grinding corn, skinning deer, and weaving, while a papoose hangs on the tree branch. (Courtesy of the American Museum of Natural History.)

27. A war club used in hand-to-hand combat before the tomahawk was invented. The club which this drawing depicts is owned by the Denver Art Museum.

28. Iroquois husk mask representing the male agricultural spirit. This is a drawing of a mask which is displayed at the Peabody Museum in Cambridge, Massachusetts.

29. Iroquois turtle-shell rattle, used as a strength-giving symbol in religious ceremonies. The rattle which this drawing depicts is owned by the Peabody Museum in Cambridge, Massachusetts.

31. Big Turtle was holding a whole island on his back. A drawing by Gobin Stair.

35. Sosano-wo blowing a storm over the ocean. (Reproduced from *Kamiyo no masagoto Tokwa-gusa,* by Tominobu Hosada, Kyoto, 1827. Courtesy of the East Asiatic Library, Columbia University.)

38. Izanami and Izanagi creating an island out of sea water. (Courtesy of the Museum of Fine Arts, Boston.)

40. The gods light a bonfire before the cave in which Amaterasu is hiding. (Reproduced from *Kamiyo no masagoto Tokwa-gusa,* by Tominobu Hosada, Kyoto, 1827. Courtesy of the East Asiatic Library, Columbia University.)

41. The gods entice Amaterasu with a merry dance. (Reproduced from *Kamiyo no masagoto Tokwa-gusa,* by Tominobu Hosada, Kyoto, 1827. Courtesy of the East Asiatic Library, Columbia University.)

44. The gods build a fire, decorate the trees, and dance. The Sun Goddess is curious, opens the cave, and the gods pull her out. (Reproduced from *Mythology of All Races,* vol. VIII, edited by Canon John A. MacCulloch, Boston: Marshall Jones Co., 1928. Courtesy of the Macmillan Co.)

47. Iceland's great volcano Hekla in eruption. (Courtesy of the United Press Association.)

49. A copy of an old drawing of a Norseman's Idea of the Universe. The flat earth is surrounded by mountains; the home of the gods is on the central mountain; the cosmic tree, Yggdrasil, has branches which reach

high over the sky and roots which spread out under the earth. There is also the rainbow bridge for the gods. (Reproduced from *The Book of Earths* by Edna Kenton, New York: 1928. Courtesy of William Morrow and Co.)

55. The symbol of the Yang and Yin — the cosmic egg. (Reproduced from *Outlines of Chinese Symbolism,* by A. A. S. Williams, Peiping: Customs College Press, 1931. Courtesy of the East Asiatic Library, Columbia University.)

57. P'an Ku chiseling out the universe with the dragon, the sacred phoenix and the turtle helping. (Reproduced from *Outlines of Chinese Symbolism,* by A. A. S. Williams, Peiping: Customs College Press, 1931. Courtesy of the East Asiatic Library, Columbia University.)

58. The sacred phoenix. (Reproduced from *Mythology of All Races,* vol. VIII, edited by Canon John A. MacCulloch, Boston: Marshall Jones Co., 1928. Courtesy of the Macmillan Co.)

61. The dragon, the symbol of power and protection. (Reproduced from *Mythology of All Races,* vol. VIII, edited by Canon John A. MacCulloch, Boston: Marshall Jones Co., 1928. Courtesy of the Macmillan Co.)

62. A statue of a Sumerian gentleman who lived some four thousand years ago. (Courtesy of the University Museum, University of Pennsylvania.)

65. A Sumerian tablet recording part of the stories of The Creation, and The Flood. (Courtesy of the University Museum, University of Pennsylvania.)

67. Marduk and Tiamat in battle. An etching, some three thousand years old, engraved on two stone slabs found in the ruins of Babylon. (Reproduced from *The Babylonian Genesis,* by Alexander Heidel, Chicago: University of Chicago Press, 1942.)

71. Part of the fourth Sumerian Tablet of Creation. (Reproduced from *The Babylonian Genesis,* by Alexander Heidel, Chicago; University of Chicago Press, 1942.)

78. A copy of an old drawing of the ancient Hebrews' idea of the universe. (Reproduced from *The Earliest Cosmologies,* by William F. Warren, Cincinnati: Eaton and Mains, 1909. Courtesy of Union Theological Seminary Library.)

80. The first two days of Creation, as pictured in the Coverdale Bible, the first complete Bible printed in English, in the year 1535 A.D. (Courtesy of the New York Public Library.)

81. The third and fourth days of Creation. (Courtesy of the New York Public Library.)

82. The fifth and sixth days of Creation. (Courtesy of the New York Public Library.)

87. Adam and Eve tried to hide among the trees. A painting by Julius Schnorr, 1794-1872. (Reproduced from *The Bible and Its Story*, vol. I, edited by Charles F. Horne and Julius A. Bewer, New York: Frances R. Niglutsch, 1906. Courtesy of Union Theological Seminary Library.)

91. The Mayan Creators resting. Sometimes the Mayans thought of the Creator as two gods, male and female. Here they are pictured resting under the great cosmic tree after finishing creation. (Reproduced from *A Primer of Mayan Hieroglyphics*, by permission of Daniel G. Brinton and Ginn and Co.)

92. A Mayan temple in Yucatan. This temple is in the city of Chitzen Itza, and was centuries old when the Spaniards invaded Yucatan. (Reproduced from *Temples in Yucatan*, by Laura Gilpin, New York: Hastings House Publishers Inc., 1948.)

93. Often the Mayans thought of the Creator as a great serpent with quetzal feathers on his head and with a human face and hands. (Reproduced from *Ancient Civilizations of Mexico and Central America*, by Herbert J. Spinden, New York: 1922. Courtesy of the American Museum of Natural History.)

99. The destruction of mankind by flood, as pictured by a Mayan artist. The Creator is a serpent in the sky. From its mouth and belly water is pouring down. Two gods below are helping. (Reproduced from *The Ancient Maya*, by Sylvanus Morley, revised by George W. Brainerd, Stanford: Stanford University Press, 1956. Copyright 1956 by the Board of Trustees of Leland Stanford Junior University.)

101. Miwok Indians cracking and grinding acorns and mixing the dough. They are also basket-weaving and have been fishing. A painting by Arthur A. Jansson. (Courtesy of the American Museum of Natural History.

105. "What should man be like?" asked the Coyote. A drawing by Gobin Stair.

109. Wintu women preparing clover seeds for cooking. A drawing by E. M. Kern. (Reproduced from *History, Condition and Prospects of the Indian Tribes of the United States*, by Henry R. Schoolcraft, Philadelphia: Lippincott and Co., 1855.)

113. "What are you doing here?" asked the Coyote man. A drawing by Gobin Stair.

117. A statue of Eros, the God of Love, made in the third century b.c. (Courtesy of The Metropolitan Museum of Art.)

125. Pandora is brought to the earth by Hermes. Engraved by William Blake from compositions of John Flaxman. (Reproduced from *The Theogony — Works and Days and Days of Hesiod,* London: Longman, Hurst Rees, Orne and Brown, 1817.)

126. Pandora is presented to Epimetheus. Engraved by William Blake from compositions of John Flaxman. (Reproduced from *The Theogony — Works and Days and Days of Hesiod,* London: Longman, Hurst Rees, Orne and Brown, 1817.)

129. Pandora and Epimetheus when the jar is opened. Hope waits inside the jar, holding a flower. (Reproduced from *The Theogony — Works and Days and Days of Hesiod,* London: Longman, Hurst Rees, Orne and Brown, 1817.)

131. Zuni prayer plumes. (Courtesy of the American Museum of Natural History.)

132. An Indian pueblo today, near Taos, New Mexico. (Reproduced from *The First Penthouse Dwellers of America,* by Ruth Underhill, Santa Fe: Laboratory of Anthropology, 1945.)

133. In an Indian wigwam a Zuni priest draws a prayer picture in the sand. (Courtesy of the American Museum of Natural History.)

135. Then the Beloved Twain led all the man-creatures whom they could persuade up the vine-ladder. . . . A drawing by Gobin Stair.

149. A nebula far beyond our galaxy, seen edge on. It is named Corna Berenices. (Yerkes Observatory photograph.)

151. A nebula seen from above. It is named Ursa Major. (Yerkes Observatory photograph.)

153. Drawings of fifteen different atoms. The simplest, the hydrogen atom, is first; and the most complicated, the uranium atom, is last. (Reproduced from *The Elements: Builders of the Universe,* by Jerome S. Meyer, New York: World Publishing Co., 1958.)

165. An amoeba magnified many times. When alive it changes its shape continually. (Courtesy of Bausch and Lomb Optical Company.)

171. A glass model of a volvox enlarged from its natural size, which is about that of a grain of sand. (Courtesy of the American Museum of Natural History.)

172. Some of the early forms of life in the sea 500,000,000 years ago. (Courtesy of the American Museum of Natural History.)

179. A painting of two of the giant dinosaurs, the Tyrannosaurus and the Triceratops. (Courtesy of the American Museum of Natural History.)

180. One of the huge reptiles that turned into a bird. It is named *archaeopterix,* which means "ancient bird." Note the claws on its wings and the teeth in its mouth. (Courtesy of the Chicago Museum of Natural History.)

181. A diagram showing the most important steps in the evolution of life, and the millions of years each lasted. (Courtesy of the American Museum of Natural History.)

185. This is how one artist has imagined one of our ancestors might have looked about 20,000 years ago. (Courtesy of the British Museum of Natural History, London.)

190. The first Java men may have looked something like this. (Courtesy of the American Museum of Natural History.)

193. A bear invades the cave of a Neanderthal man and woman. A painting by F. L. Jacques. (Courtesy of the American Museum of Natural History.)

195. The model of a cave where Cro-Magnon artists etched and painted their rock pictures, 20,000 years ago. (Courtesy of the American Museum of Natural History.)

197. Two wild deer talking together. Painted in color by a Cro-Magnon artist in the cave near Font-de-Gaume, France. (Courtesy of the American Museum of Natural History.)

Suggested Bibliography for Supplementary Reading

Andrews, Roy Chapman. *Meet Your Ancestors.* New York, Viking Press, 1948. Short, interestingly written account of recent discoveries.

Bandi, Hans Georg, and Maringer, Johannes. *Art in the Ice Age.* New York, Frederick A. Praeger, 1955. An expensive book, beautifully illustrated.

Barnett, Lincoln. *The World We Live In. Special Edition for Young Readers.* A Golden Book. New York, Simon and Schuster, 1956. A large book, beautifully illustrated, filled with interesting details regarding theories of the beginnings of earth, sky, and life.

Baumann, Hans. *The Caves of the Great Hunters.* Translated from the German by Isabel and Florence McHugh. New York, Pantheon Books, 1954. A fascinating story of the discovery of the art of the cave dwellers, with a fine interpretation of their significance.

Benedict, Ruth. *Patterns of Culture. An Analysis of Our Social Structure as Related to Primitive Civilizations*. New York, Penguin Books, 1947. Chapter IV describes the Zuni life and customs.

Berndt, Ronald and Catherine. *The First Australians*. New York, Philosophical Library, 1954. A short popular book by two anthropologists.

Boeke, Kees. *Cosmic View*. New York, John Day Company, 1957.

Boer, Friederich, ed. *Igloos, Yurts, and Totem Poles*. Translated from the German by Florence McHugh. New York, Pantheon Books, 1957. Chapter I is on the Australian aborigines.

Clark, Lou. *Your How the World Began*. Chicago, Children's Press, 1957. Easy to understand and profusely illustrated.

Coon, Carleton S. *The Story of Man*. New York, Alfred A. Knopf, 1954. An interesting continued story of mankind's evolution.

Engel, Leonard, ed. *New Worlds of Modern Science*. New York, Dell Publishing Company, 1956. Paper back. Contains one chapter on Gamow's theory of creation.

Epstein, Sam and Beryl. *Prehistoric Animals*. New York, Franklin Watts, 1956. Story of evolution from one-celled forms through to man.

Fenton, Carroll Lane. *Life Long Ago: The Story of Fossils*. New York, John Day, 1937. An excellent resource book, with many drawings and photos.

Fergusson, Erna. *Dancing Gods*. New York, Alfred A. Knopf, 1931. Chapter II describes five different dances of Zunis.

Fergusson, Erna. *Guatemala*. New York, Alfred A. Knopf, 1939. An interesting book on the Mayans, ancient and modern.

Gallant, Roy A. *Exploring the Universe*. Garden City, Doubleday and Company, 1956. Beautifully illustrated and clearly written.

Gamow, George. *The Creation of the Universe*. New York, Viking, 1952. Gives Gamow's theory of beginnings, spelled out in full.

Grant, Madeleine F. *Wonder World of Microbes*. New York, Whittlesey House, 1956. A fascinating account of the activities of these microscopic life forms, written by a professor of biology at Sarah Lawrence College.

Haber, Heinz. *Our Friend the Atom*. New York, Simon and Schuster, 1956. Illustrated by Walt Disney Studios. Available in paper back.

Hooton, Earnest A. *Up from the Ape*. Cambridge, Harvard University Press, 1945. Rather difficult reading.

Howells, William. *Mankind So Far*. Volume V in History Series of American Museum of Natural History. Garden City, Doubleday, Doran and Company, 1945.

Hoyle, Fred. *The Nature of the Universe.* New York, Harper & Brothers, 1950. Presentation of the second theory proposed by scientists.

Hyde, Margaret Q. *Atoms — Today and Tomorrow.* New York, Whittlesey House, 1955. For older boys and girls. Clear and accurate.

Krutch, Joseph Wood. *The Great Chain of Life.* Cambridge, Riverside Press, 1956. Fascinating sketches of steps in the evolution of life, presented with a warmth of empathy, by a naturalist and writer.

La Barre, Weston. *The Human Animal.* Chicago, University of Chicago Press, 1954. A challenging portrayal of the story of man's evolution.

Langdon, Stephen H. *Babylonian Epic of Creation.* Oxford, Clarendon Press, Ltd., 1923.

Leach, Marie. *The Beginning: Creation Myths Around the World.* New York, Funk and Wagnalls, 1956. An interesting collection, edited by a professional folk-lorist. Among the myths are versions of the Zuni, Seneca Indian, Mayan Indian, Bushman, and Sumerian stories.

Lewellen, John. *The Mighty Atom.* New York, Alfred A. Knopf, 1955. Easy reading for younger readers.

Love, J. R. B. *Stone Age Bushmen of Today.* London, Blackie and Son, Ltd., 1936. These are the Australian aborigines.

Luquet, Georges H. *The Art and Religion of Fossil Man.* Translated from the French by J. Townsend Russell. New Haven, Yale University Press, 1930.

Marrett, R. R. *Faith, Hope and Charity in Primitive Religion.* New York, Macmillan, 1932.

Marrett, R. R. *Sacraments of Primitive Folk.* New York, Oxford University Press, 1933. These two books by Marrett, a professor of anthropology at Oxford University, reveal a rare combination of psychological understanding and religious sensitivity.

Mendelsohn, Isaac, ed. *Religions of the Ancient Near East.* New York, Liberal Arts Press, 1955. Contains E. A. Speiser's translation of the Sumerian-Babylonian story and a full description of the New Year's Festival in Babylon where it was annually dramatized.

Meyer, Jerome S. *The Elements: Builders of the Universe.* New York, World Publishing Company, 1958.

Montagu, Ashley. *Man: His First Million Years. A Primer of Anthropology.* Cleveland, World Book Company, 1957. A dramatically written story.

Mountford, Charles P. *Brown Men and Red Sand. Journeyings in Wild Australia.* London, Phoenix House, Ltd., 1950. A small book, illustrated with excellent photographs, written by an anthropologist who both enjoys and respects the Australian aborigines.

Schealer, John M. *The Way to the Stars*. New York, E. P. Dutton and Company, 1957. Interesting introduction to astronomy with many illustrations and diagrams.

Scheele, William E. *Prehistoric Man and the Primates*. Cleveland, World Publishing Company, 1957. Contains 100 drawings by the author, who is director of the Cleveland Museum of Natural History.

Shapley, Harlow. *Of Stars and Men*. Boston, Beacon Press, 1958. A distinctive scientific discussion for the layman.

Spinden, Herbert J. *Maya Art and Civilization*. Indian Hills, Colorado, Falcon's Wing Press, 1950. An expensive, beautifully illustrated book by the former Curator of American Indian Art at the Brooklyn Museum.

Thompson, J. Eric. *The Civilization of the Mayans*. Chicago, Chicago Museum of Natural History Press, 1936. A paper-bound illustrated book that gives a brief and clear account of the Mayans.

Wendt, Herbert. *In Search of Adam*. Translated from the German by James Cleugh. Boston, Houghton Mifflin Company, 1956. A popular narrative of the discoveries of prehistoric man.

Windels, Fernand. *The Lascaux Cave Paintings*. New York. Viking Press, 1950. A very beautiful book of photographs of the paintings in the cave discovered in 1940 by four boys. Windels calls the cave "the hunters' sanctuary."